A New Mathematics Reader

Evelyn Sharp

A NEW MATHEMATICS READER

New York / E. P. Dutton & Co., Inc.

 / Library of Congress catalog card number: 67–20141 / Published simultaneously in Canada by Clarke, Irwin & Company Limited, Toronto and Vancouver.

FIRST EDITION

CONTENTS

FOREWORD

I don't know whether you are like the students in my math classes, but whenever a new topic comes up in their textbooks the question I hear most often is "What are they talking about?" Exactly which topics in any of the current series of excellent texts draw this comment will vary, depending on the student's background in mathematics. But, sooner or later, this same question gets asked by somebody about almost every topic.

The purpose of this book is to explain to you in everyday, informal language something of "What they are talking about." Then, armed with this beginning, you will be better able to tackle the more technical wording of your textbooks.

Some of these topics you will probably meet in the seventh grade, if not sooner. Others come later on in high school, all the way up to the senior year. A few, such as game theory, are too new to be part of the regular curriculum yet. I have included them in order to give you a taste of what is going on out near the frontiers of mathematics.

School mathematics is in a period of change—a time of

acceleration and upgrading. Not only are new topics being added, but the level of the courses has been raised. In senior high school you are asked to master math that, a few years ago, was taught only in college. Similarly, some senior high school courses have been moved into the junior high school.

You do not master mathematics by simply memorizing formulas and rules. Mastery calls for insight into the overall pattern. I have noticed that the students who find math easiest are those who, when confronted with a new topic, turn it over and over in their minds, hunting for the spot where it hooks on to the rest of mathematics, and then nail it firmly into place. They can walk around in the whole structure at will. The people who have trouble with math are the ones who see, not a structure, but a pile of unrelated facts.

In this book I have tried to help you find out how some of the different parts of mathematics fit together. It is intended as background reading for students anywhere in the seventh through twelfth grades, according to the need. Or, if you are interested in math, you can just pick up the book and start reading, regardless of what class you are in. I hope it will aid you in reaching your goal and possibly provide a little enjoyment along the way.

EVELYN SHARP

September, 1967

A New Mathematics Reader

PART I

1

Sets—The Root of It All

What is the new mathematics like? At its core is the set concept, an idea at once simple enough to be grasped by a beginner and so all-pervading that you can't understand modern mathematics without it.

A set is just what you think it is: a group of things that are considered together in some way. You can speak of a set of chairs, a set of people, or a set of numbers. If you look on this ____________ as just a line, you may be dreadfully old-fashioned. It's an illustration of a set of points.

For the student, sets offer clarity, simplification, and a method of unifying diverse fragments of knowledge. This single thread runs through arithmetic, algebra, geometry, and such new branches of higher mathematics as topology.

One of the applications of set theory is in Boolean algebra, so named for George Boole, an English mathematician who pioneered in the study of symbolic logic. It has been useful in the development of high-speed electronic digital computers—the electronic brains—where it provides a tangible and workable method of analyzing the myriad electric circuits involved. Actually, Boolean algebra had been lying around in the attic of pure mathematics for about a century (George Boole died before Abraham Lincoln did) until the dictates of the machines brought it downstairs.

Equivalent Sets

Sets are equivalent if they each have the same number of objects, in which case they are said to be in one-to-one correspondence. It is not necessary to know how to count to recognize this. Suppose you had a picture of two monkeys and two bananas, with directions to match them one-to-one, meaning give a banana to each monkey. No resemblance between the objects in the different sets is implied. They are alike only in their twoness.

If you had enough pictures, each showing a different number of monkeys, and only one showing a collection of bananas, you could hunt around until you found a monkey set that matched the set of bananas. Even a savage or a small child could do this. It is an intuitive concept and has nothing to do with knowing the names of the numbers or, really, in what order they come. Arranging them in order is the second step. In such a way all of mathematics can be built up.

Set Membership

A set can contain any number of members, from zero on up. If I speak of the set of all the red-haired people in this block and it happens that everybody in the neighborhood is either blond or brunette, that's still all right—I have an empty set and its symbol is ϕ. This is not as whimsical as it seems. An empty box is not the same as no box at all. The empty set (also called "null set") is simply the set that has no elements.

Membership in a set is denoted by ϵ, the Greek letter epsilon. If you have a set of dogs, K (sets are often named by capital letters), then Rover ϵ K. This is read: "Rover is an element of set K," or "Rover is a member of set K." If there is a flea on one of the dogs, the flea is not a member of the set. True, he is *there,* but he is not a member—he is an interloper. This would be indicated by writing: flea $\notin K$.

Notice K is not the set of *all* dogs, just the ones in some specific category—maybe those you see out your window. Write it:

$$K = \{\text{Rover, Fido, Lassie}\}$$

This works fine for a small number, but suppose you want to make a set of all the dogs in the Kennel Club show. It would be extremely tedious and impractical to list them by the roster method. The set of all the dogs in the United States would be downright impossible to write that way. Instead, a large set is described by setting down the rule for membership.

$$K = \{\text{all the dogs in the U.S.}\}$$

More properly, it's given this way:

$$K = \{x \mid x \text{ is a dog in the U.S.}\}$$

In mathematical jargon this is read: "The set of all x such that x is a dog in the United States." The vertical bar $\mid$ is translated: "such that."

PROBLEMS

1. List the members of the following set:

$$A = \{x \mid x \text{ is an odd number between 0 and 10}\}$$

2. Write the following set by the rule method:

$A =$ {Sunday, Monday, Tuesday, Wednesday, Thursday, Friday, Saturday}

3. Write the set of all major-league baseball players whose batting average is above .500.

4. What is the name of the figure described in this set?

$A =$ {in a plane, all points 2 inches from a given point}

Subsets

Just as committees have subcommittees, sets have subsets. Starting with $X = \{1,2,3\}$ I can pick any elements of the set I like for a subset–$\{1\}$, or $\{2,3\}$ or $\{3\}$, etc. By convention, every set is a subset of itself, that is $\{1,2,3\}$ is a subset of set X. This is stretching a point, but that's the way it is done to achieve consistency.

The null set is also a subset of every set. This is logical if you consider that I might be finicky when I am choosing the members to make a subset and not choose any of them. Then I would have an empty set, but it is still counted as a legal subset.

There is a short-cut way of predicting how many subsets there will be in the bureaucracy. In the example above, I predict there will be eight. Listing them, there are $\{1\}$, $\{2\}$, $\{3\}$, $\{1,2\}$, $\{1,3\}$, $\{2,3\}$, $\{1,2,3\}$, ϕ. How did I know? I cubed 2, that is took $2 \times 2 \times 2$, which is eight–cubed because the original set had three members. In the set $\{3,5,7,9\}$ I predict there will be sixteen, or 2 raised to the fourth power. Write all the possibilities down and count them if you don't believe me. It works every time. In general, the number of subsets is 2^n, n being the number of elements of the original set.

To indicate that one set is a subset of another, you use the symbol $A \subset B$, read: "A is a subset of B," or "A is contained in B." $B \supset A$ says the same thing in reverse order, that is: "B contains A."

PROBLEMS

In problems 1, 2, and 3 let set A consist of one coin of each denomination, U.S. currency, in use at the present time (excluding the silver dollar).

1. How many subsets are there of set A?
2. How many of these subsets each have an aggregate value of 60 cents or more?
3. Write the eight subsets of the set $\{x,y,z\}$

Is each of the following statements true or false?

4. If $A \subset B$ and $B \subset A$, then $A = B$
5. If $A \subset B$ and $B \supset A$, then $A = B$
6. If $A \subset B$ and $B \subset C$ and $C \subset A$, then $B = C$

Set Operations

You don't add, subtract, multiply, or divide sets—instead, there are three fundamental operations called intersection, union, and complementation. For an example, you might begin by listing the four-legged objects in the room where you're sitting—say the sofa, the table, an armchair, and the dog. Enclose the list in braces (never parentheses or brackets, always braces) and call it set A.

$$A = \{\text{sofa, table, chair, dog}\}$$

Set B could be all the animate objects in the room—yourself, the dog, and whoever else happens to be there.

$$B = \{\text{you, dog, John, Sue}\}$$

Now the intersection of sets A and B would be the dog —he is the only one that fits both categories. In other words, he's a member of both sets. This is written:

$$A \cap B = \{\text{dog}\}$$

$\cap$ is the symbol for intersection.

$A \cap B$ is read: "the intersection of A and B" or "A cap B." Of course, if you don't have a dog, or even a cat, the intersection would be an empty set, written $A \cap B = \phi$.

The set operations are usually illustrated by drawings, called Venn diagrams after the English logician who popularized them. A Venn diagram of the problem above looks like this:

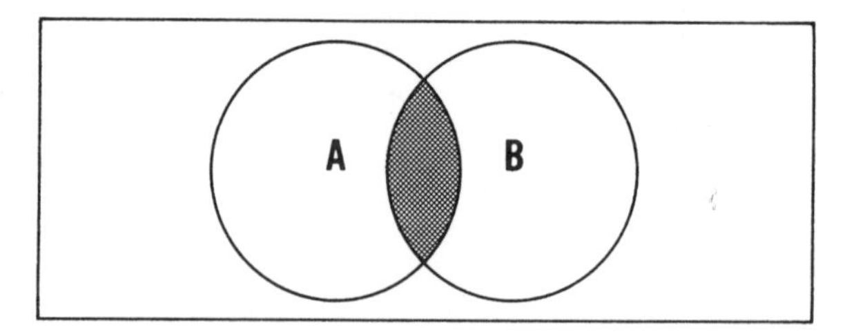

The interior of Circle A represents set A; the interior of circle B is set B. (They show the relationship between the sets—not their comparative sizes.) The shaded portion is $A \cap B$.

If the intersection is the empty set, then the circles do not overlap. In that case sets A and B are said to be disjoint.

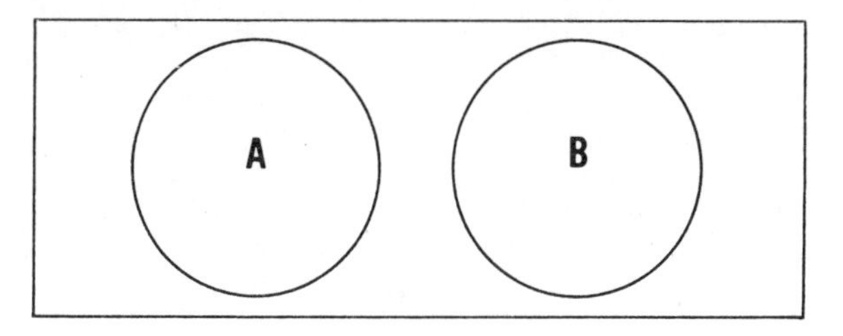

Turn $\cap$ upside down, and you have $\cup$, the symbol for union. $A \cup B$, read: "the union of A and B," or "A cup B," means all the objects contained in either set.

$$A \cup B = \{\text{sofa, table, chair, dog, you, John, Sue}\}$$

You notice you don't list the dog twice—only once. In Venn diagrams the entire shaded area represents $A \cup B$.

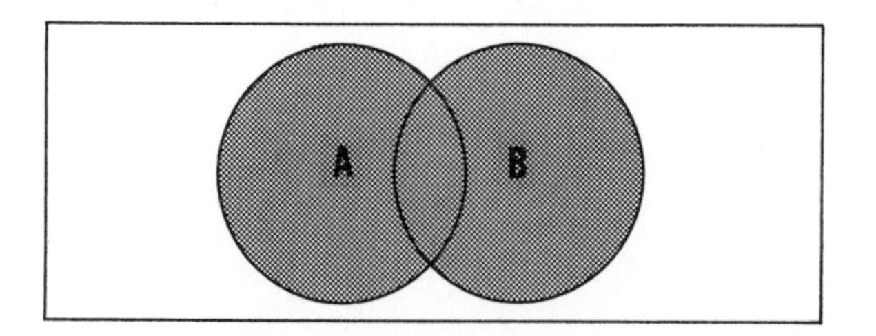

For complementation you need a set and a subset. Say set V comprises all the things you ate yesterday afternoon:

$$V = \{\text{hamburger, malt, pizza, Coke}\}$$

Then let subset A be only those that are liquid:

$$A = \{\text{malt, Coke}\}$$

The complement of set A, written A', would be all the other things:

$$A' = \{\text{hamburger, pizza}\}$$

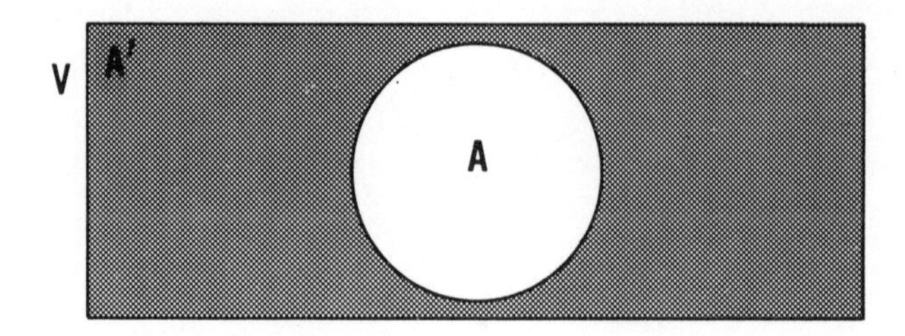

Unfortunately, the symbolism is not yet uniform. I am looking at three books—one uses A', one uses a tilde $\sim A$, and one uses $\bar{A}$ for the complement. Like the man who never knew what time it was because he had two watches, you will be better off if you pick one—the one in your textbook—and stick to it.

While sets may contain anything, in arithmetic they are most often numbers. For a sample problem, start with a fairly large collection of numbers called the universal set (usually named U, but some books say V) and two smaller ones, A and B.

$U = \{x \mid x \text{ is a whole number from 1 to 10, inclusive}\}$
$A = \{1,3,5,7\}$
$B = \{1,2,3,4\}$

The directions might say: "Write the following sets by the listing method:"

1. $A \cup B$ The solution is: $A \cup B = \{1,2,3,4,5,7\}$
2. $A \cap B$ This would be: $A \cap B = \{1,3\}$
3. A' This is: $A' = \{2,4,6,8,9,10\}$
4. $(A \cup B)'$ Worked out: $A \cup B = \{1,2,3,4,5,7\}$
   Therefore the complement is all the other numbers in the universal set or
   $(A \cup B)' = \{6,8,9,10\}$

A page of problems in Boolean algebra looks as if you had scratched them in the ground down by the stables and a sharply shod horse had walked over it. With horseshoes going north, south, east, and west it makes you think of that man who jumped on his mount and rode off in all directions.

PROBLEMS

LET: $U = \{x \mid x \text{ is a whole number from 1 to 10, inclusive}\}$
$A = \{2,4,6\}$
$B = \{4,5,6,7\}$
$C = \{3,9,10\}$

For problems 1 through 7, use the universal set and the subsets A, B, C given above.

Write the following sets by the listing method:

1. $A \cap B$
2. $B \cup C$
3. B'
4. $(A \cap B) \cup C$
5. $(A \cup B)'$
6. $(B \cup C)' \cap A$
7. $A \cap C$

Given: $A = \{\text{all points on straight line } L\}$
$B = \{\text{all points on straight line } M\}$

8. If line L and line M intersect, how many members in set $A \cap B$?
9. If lines L and M are parallel, how many members in set $A \cap B$?
10. What symbol would you use for the set described in exercise 9?

Is each of these statements true or false?

11. $(A \cap B) \subset A$
12. $A \subset (A \cup B)$

2

Relations and Functions—Two Sets Get Together

When you see the words "unknown quantity" what do you think of? A puddle of nothingness, with an x slowly forming on the surface? Modern mathematics prefers more precise notions. Instead of "unknown quantity" they use the word "variable" and give it an exact definition. A variable is a symbol (usually a letter) that stands for any one of the members of a certain set. It acts as a sort of spaceholder until one of the members of the replacement set is chosen.

Mathematical statements (such as $6 + x = 10$) are now customarily called "sentences," and if the statement contains a variable it is called an "open sentence." As it stands, an open sentence is neither true nor false, but it becomes one or the other according to which replacement is chosen for the variable. For example, use the replacement set $\{1,2,3,4,5\}$ with the open sentence given above. If the variable, x, is replaced with 4, the sentence is true. Any other choice makes it false.

Relations

Since a variable is a symbol which stands for any one of the members of a certain set, it follows that if there are two variables there must be two replacement sets. For instance, if set $A = \{\text{Tom, Dick, Harry}\}$, the variable x stands for either Tom or Dick or Harry, as the case may be. The variable y represents a member of a second set—possibly set $B = \{\text{Mary, Sue, Jane}\}$. Much of mathematics centers around the idea of pairing the members of the two sets, just as in old-fashioned musical comedy where, when the curtain went down, the situation was most likely to be {(Tom, Sue), (Dick, Mary), (Harry, Jane)}.

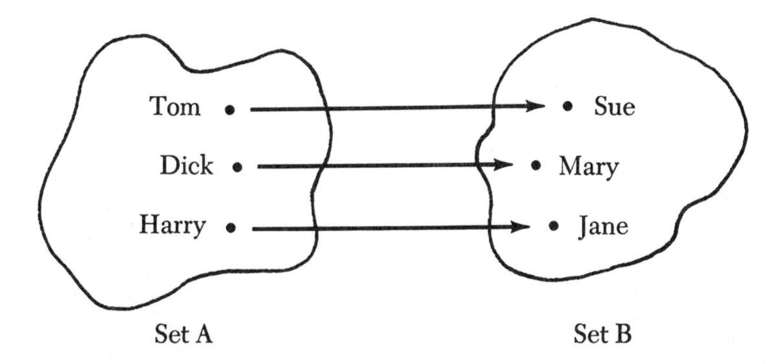

A set of such pairs is called a *relation* and the study of relations is one of the central concepts in new math, another being the set itself. These are not just new topics which have been appliquéd onto the previously existing fabric of mathematics. Rather, the whole structure has been reorganized so that it stems from these ideas.

New mathematics may be pictured as a tree with sets and relations at its roots, everything else growing out of these. Old math could not be represented as a tree at all—there was no trunk, just a lot of separate branches.

In order to generate a set of pairs (i.e., a relation) there are three necessary ingredients—a first set, called the *domain*, a second set, called the *range*, and a rule for pairing them. In mathematics these must be *ordered* pairs—that is, (1,2) is not the same as (2,1). Furthermore, the first member of the pair must come from the first set, the second from the second set.

It works like this: You, as monarch of the domain, arbitrarily select a member of the first set. The rule then swings into action like a machine and automatically picks a partner from the second set.

Sometimes these pairs are written in the form of a table, either horizontal or vertical:

x	y
6	4
7	5
8	6
10	8

x	6	7	8	10
y	4	5	6	8

Examine the relationship between the first and second members of each pair. Do you see that in this particular case the rule is: The second member of the pair is always 2 less than the first member?

Rather than using words, a rule may be more compactly stated as a formula or open sentence, using the relations symbols "=," ">" (which means "greater than") or "<" (which means "less than"). Written in this fashion the rule above is: $y = x - 2$.

A sentence, a formula, and a table are all handy devices for showing a relation, but by far the most graphic is, naturally, a graph. It gives a picture of the relation, and pictures are easier to understand than words.

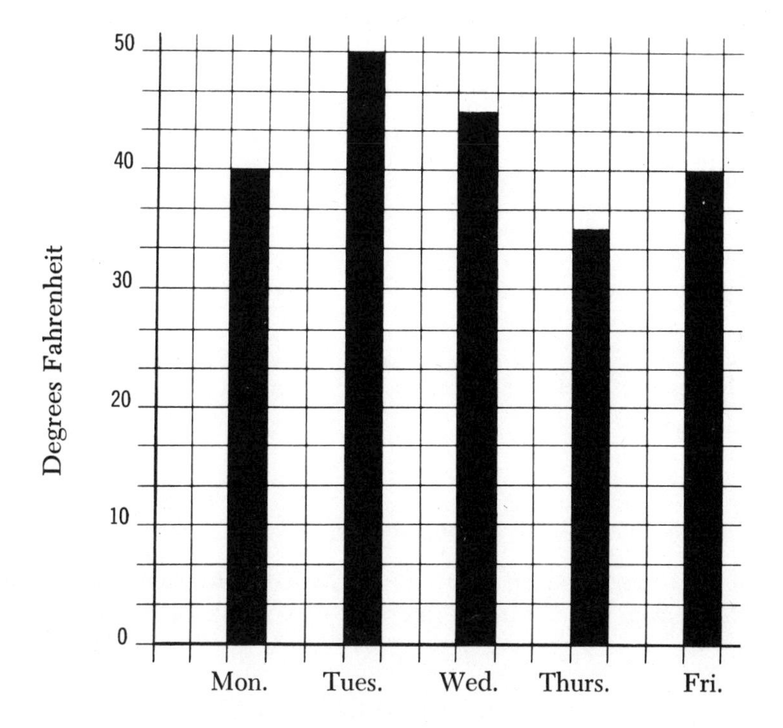

There's nothing new about bar graphs of this kind. You see them in newspapers, magazines, geographies, etc., and they have been part of the arithmetic course for years. What *is* new is their use in showing ordered pairs. The graph on this page is a picture of a relation—i.e., the set of ordered pairs: (Monday, 40°), (Tuesday, 50°), (Wednesday, 45°), (Thursday, 35°), (Friday, 40°).

Relations are not always this simple. Suppose that instead

of the pairs (Tom, Sue), (Dick, Mary), (Harry, Jane) mentioned at the beginning of this section, you consider a country and a time where plural wives were the rule. Then, if set $A = \{$Abdul, Hassim$\}$ and set $B = \{$Fatima, Leyla, Ayshe, Scheherazade$\}$ the pairs might turn out to be (Abdul, Fatima), (Abdul, Leyla), (Hassim, Ayshe), (Hassim, Scheherazade). Here a member of the first set is partnered with two different members of the second set.

This same thing can happen with numbers. Take this example:

$$\text{Set } A = \{3,4\}$$
$$\text{Set } B = \{1,2,3\}$$

Rule: The first member of the pair must be larger than the second member.

The set of ordered pairs is: $\{(3,1), (3,2), (4,1), (4,2), (4,3)\}$.

PROBLEMS

1. Given the following ordered pairs, what is the domain set? The range set? Write the rule in words, and as a formula.

$$(1,2), (2,4), (3,6), (4,8), (5,10)$$

2. What is the rule connecting the two sets shown in this table?

x	y
1	3
2	5
4	9
5	11

3. Given the following sets and rule, make a table showing all possible ordered pairs:

$$\text{First set} = \{1,2,3\}$$
$$\text{Second set} = \{0,1\}$$

Rule: The second member of each pair must be smaller than the first member.

Functions

In the preceding section, you saw examples of two different types of relations—one was the set of ordered pairs {(Tom, Sue), (Dick, Mary), (Harry, Jane)}; the other was the set of ordered pairs {(Abdul, Fatima), (Abdul, Leyla), (Hassim, Ayshe), (Hassim, Scheherazade)}.

The first of these types is a special kind of relation called a *function.* In a function, when the first member of the pair is chosen, the rule then inexorably designates one, and only one, possible partner. In the example about Abdul and Fatima, this is not the case, since Abdul is paired with two different partners.

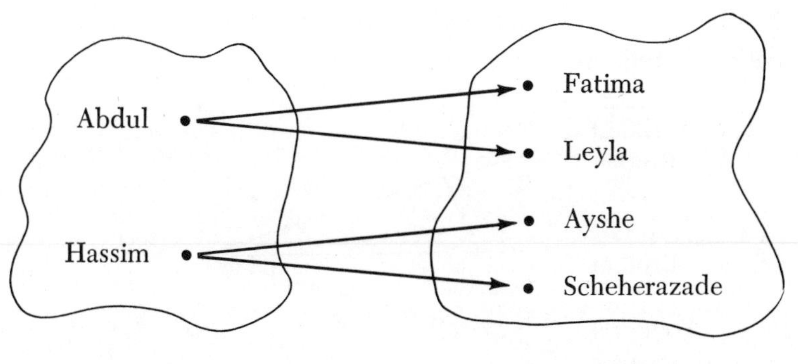

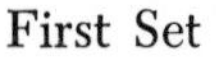

Second Set

This is a relation (any set of ordered pairs is a relation), but it is not a function. Incidentally, the words *relation* and *function* have precise mathematical meanings which you could not deduce from their use in ordinary conversation. A function is defined as a relation in which no two different ordered pairs have the same first member.

Don't jump to the conclusion that, in a function, the pairing must be entirely monogamous. For instance, take an example from Tibet where, in a sort of package deal, when a woman marries a man she sometimes marries his brothers also. They then form a single household—the brothers, all of whom are her husbands, and the one wife (let's name her Yamo). In such a case, the first set might be {Eldest Brother, Middle Brother, Youngest Brother} and the second set contain only {Yamo}. The pairs are: {(Eldest Brother, Yamo), (Middle Brother, Yamo), (Youngest Brother, Yamo)}. This is a function, even though Yamo appears in three different pairs.

What's the difference between this and the example about Abdul and Fatima? It's not the fact that one is polyandry and the other polygamy. From a mathematical standpoint, this has nothing to do with it. The reason that the Tibet example fits the definition of a function is that once Eldest Brother is picked from the *first* set, his partner is automatically pointed out. There is no ambiguity.

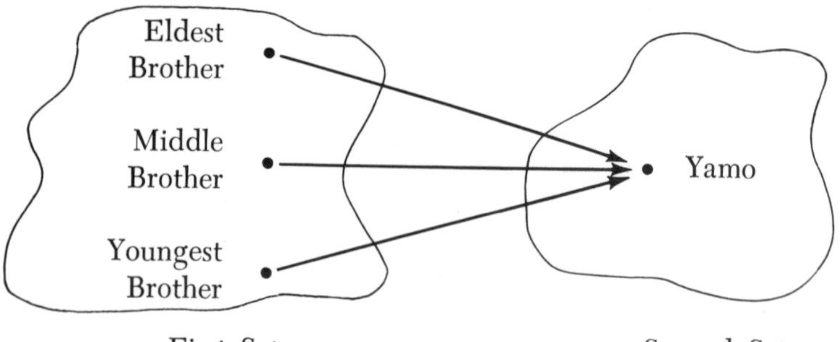

True, if a different brother is selected, the path also leads straight to the same partner. However, as the mathematician looks at the situation, always starting with a member of the *first* set, there is still no ambiguity. If he picks Eldest Brother, the second member of the pair is, without doubt, Yamo. On the other hand if he picks Abdul, the second member of the pair may be Fatima or it may be Leyla.

Illustrated with numbers, this set of ordered pairs is a function: $\{(3,5), (2,5), (4,6)\}$. This set is not: $\{(1,2), (1,3), (4,6)\}$. The ability to distinguish functions from other types of relations is important in algebra and higher mathematics.

In functional notation an "f" (for function) is written in front of another symbol, which may be either a numeral or a letter—for example, f(4). This is read "f of 4." The rule for pairing the members of two sets may be thought of as a sort of machine. "f of 4" means "This is the result that comes out of the function machine when a 4 is fed into it." If the machine is operating according to a "Multiply by three" rule, what comes out is a 12. Therefore, in this case, f(4) is 12.

If a 5 were fed into this function machine, out would come a 15—the f(5). Arranged in a table, some examples of the input and output of this particular machine might be:

x	f(x)
4	12
5	15
6	18
7	21

Notice that functional notation, used in this way, eliminates the need for y as a symbol for the second member of each pair, as you can see by comparing this table with the one on page 22. $f(x)$ is used instead of y as the heading of the second column. In the mathematics of relations, these two symbols are interchangeable—just take your choice.

PROBLEMS

1. If a function machine is operating according to the rule "Add three," find the following:
   a. $f(1)$
   b. $f(2)$
   c. $f(0)$
   d. $f(4)$

2. Are these sets of ordered pairs functions?
   a. $\{(1,3), (2,4), (5,7), (6,8)\}$
   b. $\{(1,3), (1,4), (5,7), (5,8)\}$
   c. $\{(4,2), (3,2), (6,5), (8,5)\}$

Inverse Relations

Maybe—because of the emphasis placed on the *order* of the members in each pair—you are curious about what would happen if this order were changed. The answer is: You get an *inverse relation.*

Using the function machine which yielded the ordered pair (4,12), suppose we start by feeding a 12 into it, already knowing that a 4 must come out. Do you see that the function rule will have to be changed to achieve the pair (12,4)? Instead of "Multiply by three" it must become "Divide by three." Division is the inverse process from multiplication.

In the same way, if the machine had been operating under

an "Add five" rule–giving pairs like (2,7), (3,8), (4,9)–switching the order in all these pairs to (7,2), (8,3), (9,4) will necessitate changing the rule to "Subtract five." There is an inverse relationship between addition and subtraction –that is, one undoes the other. Therefore the new set of ordered pairs (7,2), (8,3), (9,4), obtained by interchanging the members of each original pair, is called an inverse relation.

When you judge whether these inverses fit into the special category of relations called functions, bear in mind that each inverse must stand on its own feet. That is, just because the original set of ordered pairs was a function, it does not necessarily follow that its inverse is also a function. The definition of a function specifies that no two different ordered pairs have the same *first* member and, when the order is switched around, you now have different first members.

PROBLEMS

1. Given this relation: $\{(1,4), (3,6), (5,8), (7,10)\}$ write the inverse relation.

2. a. What is the rule connecting the first and second members of each pair in the relation in problem 1?
   b. What is the rule connecting the first and second members of each pair in the inverse relation in your answer to problem 1?

3. The following sets of ordered pairs are functions. Which ones have inverses that are also functions?
   a. $\{(0,2), (1,4), (2,6)\}$
   b. $\{(0,3), (1,3), (2,5)\}$
   c. $\{(2,4), (3,9), (-2,4)\}$

3

Logic—How to Reason in Symbols

When the average person says something is logical, he means it is reasonable, or commonsensical, or in accord with the known facts of the situation. When a mathematician uses the word, he is talking about something completely different. The meaning he intends to convey may have nothing to do with the actual state of physical affairs, but only that the thing conforms to the rules of the formal subject of logic. It is an attempt to codify the most intuitive forms of human reasoning. Doing a textbook exercise in logic requires a performance as stylized as that of a Javanese temple dancer.

The origins of the subject go back to Aristotle, and it was held in high regard during the Middle Ages. What qualifies logic as "new" math is the fact that about a hundred years ago symbols were introduced into it by George Boole, De Morgan, and others. (A hundred years is recent, compared to Aristotle's more than two thousand.) Mathematicians distrust words with their elusive connotations which change through the years—they prefer to communicate in symbols. It is symbolic logic that is a branch of the new math.

This subject has burgeoned enormously in the past twenty-five years, and its content and literature are extensive. There is a specialized research publication—the *Journal of Symbolic Logic*—devoted exclusively to articles on this topic. However, the part with which school mathematics is concerned is not difficult—it is the subject often called the algebra of logic or, sometimes, the algebra of propositions.

Possibly symbolic logic has become so popular because it can be applied to computers, in which a large number of circuits controlled by switches have to be analyzed. There is a close analogy between an electric switch, which has only two possible positions—open or closed—and a proposition in logic, which has just two possible labels—true or false. Furthermore, compound switches are built out of simple switches in the same way that compound propositions are built out of simple propositions, and calculating machines are put together out of compound electric switches (or their electronic equivalents).

Logical reasoning is the process of combining given propositions into other propositions and then doing this over and over again. Logic gives the rules of procedure. These same rules hold for compound switches, which are but the hardware embodiment of the patterns of logic.

The fact that electric switches will fit into the same formulas as those used in the algebra of propositions was first discovered by Claude E. Shannon in 1938. One result of this discovery is that symbolic logic can be used to solve the problem of designing a switching circuit to meet certain specifications, for example, in telephone dialing, computers, and vending machines. Possibly of more significance, the application also works the other way—that is, switching circuits can be used to solve logical problems. Hence machines can carry out some of the logical operations we call *deductive* reasoning, a process in which we begin with certain terms, definitions and postulates and then, proceeding always in accordance with the rules of logic, prove that a definite conclusion necessarily follows—in other words, that the conclusion is guaranteed.

Contrasted to this, in *inductive* reasoning a number of specific examples are accumulated and from them an attempt is made to reach a conclusion that will hold for all cases. The latter method should be used with caution because the conclusion is never absolutely certain, even if a thousand cases have come out the same way—the thousand and first might be different.

It is deductive reasoning that is most often used in mathematics, where "proof" usually means deductive proof. In the past, this technique has been left largely to incidental learning, at least until the formal course in geometry is reached in the tenth grade. But, since the idea of proof is basic to mathematics and to science, if mathematical logic is presented early in a student's career, it can provide a background for much that follows.

Mathematical logic is built of statements. Not questions—"Is the roast done?" or exclamations—"Happy day!" but always statements—"Today is Wednesday." If you are in doubt as to whether a given sentence is a statement or not, the test is: Can it be labeled true or false? You, personally, might not possess the necessary information to decide which is which, but if it can be said that a particular sequence of words is true (or false), then it is a statement.

Many texts call them propositions, and they are customarily represented by the lower-case letters, p, q, r, etc. These propositions are strung together according to certain fixed patterns, and then a decision is made. This decision is always either that the new statement compounded from the initial ones is true, or that it is false. It is never "maybe."

You are not free to make this decision by merely following your own interpretation of the meaning of the new statement, which would be a subjective judgment and liable to error. In fact, the study of logic is meant to lead you to replace "that which convinces me" with "that which satisfies the laws of logic." The truth or falsity of the new statement is determined according to the pattern in which the initial statements were combined. These patterns are rigid, stylized, and may be reduced to mathematical formulas. Five of the fundamental ones are: conjunction, disjunction, negation, the conditional, and the biconditional.

Conjunction

The simplest way of connecting two statements is by the word "and." For example, "Today is Wednesday and the bus is late." If both the original statements are true, the compound statement is true, obviously. If both the originals are false, so is the resulting sentence. But suppose one is true and the other false? Say today is really *Thursday* and the bus is late. Or, it's Wednesday, all right, but the bus isn't late—it's just that your watch is fast. Then is the whole statement "Today is Wednesday and the bus is late" true or false? You really would like to label it "half true," but Aristotle had no such category. Either it is 100% true, or you toss it in the "false" bin.

Tabulated, here are the rules for conjunction (call "Today is Wednesday" statement p, and "The bus is late" statement q):

p	q	p and q
True	True	True
True	False	False
False	True	False
False	False	False

In symbolic logic $\wedge$ means "and." Notice that $\wedge$ is very much like $\cap$, the symbol for intersection of sets, except that the top is pointed instead of rounded. There is some similarity between the pattern of conjunction in logic and the operation of set intersection. In both cases the key word is *and*.

To illustrate, look at the diagram on page 16. Suppose it is a dart board and we are playing a game where the winner is the one who with a single throw pierces both sets A and B. Do you see that in order to win your dart will have to stick in the shaded area where sets A and B intersect?

The neatest and most compact way of summarizing relationships is by means of a truth table, using symbols:

p	q	$p \wedge b$
T	T	T
T	F	F
F	T	F
F	F	F

PROBLEMS

Let p stand for the statement, "Jack is 42 years old," and q for the statement, "Mary is 39."

1. Write the compound sentence which is the conjunction of these two statements.
2. Write the same thing in symbols.
3. Suppose Jack really is 42, but Mary is 45 if she's a day. Is the conjunction true or false?

Disjunction

In this pattern the connecting word is "or." Bear in mind that in elementary logic "or" means "and/or." If you say, "Today is Wednesday, or the bus is late," there is no reason why both clauses can't be true.

There is no difficulty in deciding whether a statement compounded in this way is true or false. You are safe in calling it true if either or both parts are true. Only if the two initial statements are both false could the combination be false.

p	q	p or q
True	True	True
True	False	True
False	True	True
False	False	False

Condensed into a truth table, the disjunction pattern reads:

p	q	$p \vee q$
T	T	T
T	F	T
F	T	T
F	F	F

The symbol for disjunction is $\vee$, which resembles $\cup$, the symbol for union of sets. There is also a resemblance between the pattern of disjunction in logic and the operation of set union. The key word in both is *or*.

This time let's take the second diagram on page 17 as our dart board and let's say that you score by hitting set A or set B. Here the whole shaded area representing the union of the two sets is scoring territory.

In the statements used as examples, the sentence compounded from them made some sense. You wouldn't be surprised to read it in a letter, or if you saw it in print. However, this is not at all necessary in the study of logic. If "Fish swim" is statement p and "Two plus two equals four" is statement q, the validity of the various combinations can be accurately tested by the truth tables above. Grammarians might not care for sentences such as "Fish swim and two plus two equals four," but to a mathematician they are just fine.

PROBLEMS

Again let p stand for the statement "Jack is 42 years old" and q for "Mary is 39."

1. Write the compound sentence which is the disjunction of these two statements.
2. Write the disjunction in symbols.
3. Jack is telling the truth about his age, but Mary is still fibbing. Is the disjunction true or false?

Negation

Here the fixed statement "It is not true that" (or possibly "It is false that") is coupled with the initial proposition. For example, "It is not true that today is Wednesday." In everyday language this is usually telescoped into "Today is not Wednesday."

Notice that this does not tell you what today is—only that it is not Wednesday. All the days of the week are lumped into two categories:

Wednesday	Not Wednesday (Sunday, Monday, Tuesday, Thursday, Friday, Saturday)

The negation of a statement does not have to be a statement containing the word "not." If you start with "Today is not Wednesday," its negation is "It is not true that today is not Wednesday"—i.e., "Today is Wednesday."

When the first proposition is true, it automatically follows that its negation is false and vice versa. This is shown in a truth table as follows (the symbolism is not yet entirely standardized and p' is only one of the ways to write "not p"):*

p	p'
T	F
F	T

Negation is similar to complementation of sets, even to the point of using the same symbol. The key word is *not.* If you look at the diagram on page 18, you see that the shaded area represents "not A."

* Another is $\sim p$.

PROBLEMS

1. What is the negation of "Candy is fattening"?
2. Write the statement of which this is the negation: "It is not true that I own a horse."
3. Finish symbolizing the following sentences by putting in the proper symbols for the connectives:
   a. Not q
   b. p or q
   c. p and q
   d. p and not q
4. Identify the pattern of each of the following (for example, conjunction, disjunction, or negation):
   a. We do not agree.
   b. $p \vee q$
   c. It is Saturday and the rain is falling.
   d. p or q
   e. p'
   f. $p \wedge q$

The Conditional

In the fourth pattern, a pair of statements are connected by the words "if–then." (Some textbooks call conditional sentences *implications.*) For example, "If this is the end of the term, then we will have exams." Starting from the information given in the problem—this may, or may not, be the end of the term, and we may, or may not, have exams—the truth or falsity of the compound statement is then determined. Bear in mind that you are not to draw a conclusion as to the truth of one statement from what you know about the other. The truth or falsity of each of the two statements, separately, is already given. You are merely to decide on the validity of the whole sentence made by combining them in this pattern. (The "if" statement is called the *antecedent* and the "then" statement is called the *consequent.*)

Tabulating the four possible combinations, they are:

End of term	We will have exams
True	True
True	False
False	True
False	False

The symbol used in the conditional pattern is an arrow. "If p, then q" is indicated by $p \rightarrow q$. Stated in symbols, this truth table gives the logician's decision as to the truth or falsity of each of the four possible combinations above:

p	q	$p \rightarrow q$
T	T	T
T	F	F
F	T	T
F	F	T

In the first two cases the logician's decision is compatible with what we usually call common sense. Most people would agree that a compound statement made by combining two true parts would, without a doubt, be true. Also, in the second case, that if you start with a true "if" proposition and then, somehow, get off the track and follow it with a false consequent, the whole sentence would be false.

But when the logician calls both the third and fourth cases true, the gulf between intuition and the formal rules of logic becomes apparent. Perhaps it is best just to accept these as arbitrary definitions on the logician's part, although I could, by reaching, come up with an illustration for the fourth case that might satisfy you. Suppose Joe, who has always been notoriously uncoordinated, goes out for football for the first time and, after only one week's practice, tells his father that the coach has made him the starting quarterback. When his father says, "If you are a quarterback, then I'm a monkey's uncle," his intention is quite plain. He thinks both parts of the sentence are false, but that the meaning it conveys is unmistakably true.

PROBLEMS

A man says to his girl, "If you stick with me, baby, then you'll wear mink."

1. Point out the antecedent in the sentence above.
2. Which part is the consequent?
3. Write the sentence in symbols, using p and q.
4. Suppose she does stick with him, but the only fur he ever buys her is dyed muskrat. According to the truth table, is the given conditional sentence true or false?
5. On the other hand, suppose she does not stick with him. Would a logician then call the conditional sentence true or false?

The Biconditional

Suppose that, starting with a compound statement like, "If it's a tiger, then it has teeth," you pry the two clauses loose from the "if" and the "then" and interchange them. The sentence now reads, "If it has teeth, then it's a tiger."

This second version is called the *converse* of the first and, as you see above, a converse may have quite a different meaning from the original statement.

Sometimes, though, the two parts are so truly interchangeable that the sentence works either way—for example, "If this is January, then it's the first month of the year," and its converse, "If it's the first month of the year, then this is January." Here the original statement and the converse are equally true—that is, they are if you are reading this page in January. On the other hand, if it is now July, both statements are equally false. The key word is "equally" and, in such a case, the converse and the original are called *equivalent statements.*

The logic pattern in which the truth of a conditional statement and its converse are simultaneously considered is called the *biconditional.* Instead of writing both compound statements out in full, they are customarily telescoped into a single sentence using the connective "if and only if." Think about it and you will see that "This is the first month of the year if and only if it is January" says the same thing as both the sentences above. The "if" takes care of the meaning contained in one sentence and the "only if" takes care of the other. Mathematicians use the phrase "if and only if" so much that they often write it in an abbreviated form as "iff." You seldom see this in print, however—probably because it won't get by the proofreaders.

The symbol for the biconditional is an arrow with a head on both ends. $p \longleftrightarrow q$ has essentially the same meaning as the conjunction of $p \rightarrow q$ and $q \rightarrow p$. It asserts p and q are true together, or they are false together. Therefore the biconditional statement—the whole package, that is—is true in these two cases and false in the others. Its truth table is:

p	q	$p \leftrightarrow q$
T	T	T
T	F	F
F	T	F
F	F	T

PROBLEMS

Given: The compound statement "If this is December 25, then it's Christmas."

$p =$ "This is December 25"
$q =$ "It's Christmas"

1. Write the given sentence in symbols.
2. Write in words the converse of the given statement.
3. Write the converse in symbols.
4. Are the original sentence and the converse equivalent statements?
5. Combine the original and the converse into a biconditional sentence, using the connective "if and only if."
6. Write this biconditional statement in symbols.

PART II

4

Our Number System—Real and/or Imaginary

A number line is simply a horizontal line marked off into equal intervals with the numbers named in order from left to right, smaller to larger. Such a concrete geometrical picture makes certain facts about the numbers very vivid. For instance, you can plainly see that -3 is smaller than -2 because the point for -3 is to the left of the point for -2, and that $1/5$ is larger than $3/16$ because the point for $1/5$ is to the right of the point for $3/16$.

The fact that numbers can be associated with points in order along a straight line seems so obvious that it doesn't need any comment, but in the formal study of number systems, order is one of the first properties to be examined. It means that of two numbers, a and b, a is always either greater than b, equal to b, or smaller than b. There are number systems that lack this property, as you will see later.

More than one sort of number shows up on the number line. There are whole numbers, fractions, positive numbers, negative numbers, and irrational as well as rational numbers. Some (the complex numbers) even require two number lines drawn perpendicular to each other in order to illustrate them.

All these different kinds of numbers are not the result of any one person's conscious effort, but evolved slowly and painfully over a long period of time. They are the end product of several thousand years of human thought. The order in which they are put in the school curriculum roughly parallels the historical order in which they were developed.

Natural Numbers

What are natural numbers? Those a child uses when he learns to count. I never heard one say: "1, 1½, −2, $\sqrt{3}$." They are always signless whole numbers. Savages count the same way. How high they go depends on the state of advancement of their civilization. A few primitive tribes have no word for a number beyond 3—they just say "many."

The early Greeks had names for numbers only up to a myriad (ten thousand). Then, in the third century B.C., Archimedes wrote a treatise called "The Sand Reckoner" describing a new system for generating and expressing very large numbers—large enough to count not only all the grains of sand in the whole earth, even if the seas and valleys were filled up level with the mountaintops, but all the sand in the universe, which he pictured as a sphere with a radius reaching to the stars, if it were filled up the same way. His estimate of the size of this sphere was considerably off, extending only a little beyond where we now know the planet Saturn to be, but it was huge enough to serve his purpose—namely, to show that even these gigantic quantities could be counted.

First he figured how many grains of sand placed side by side would equal the diameter of a poppy seed, then how many poppy seeds would equal a finger's breadth, and so on up. Starting from a myriad, he invented new numbers to count all this sand, arranging them into orders and periods. His first order ended with a myriad myriad, or one hundred million, which he called an octade. This then became the unit for the second order, which went up to an octade octades. The third order, in turn, climbed to an octade octade octades, etc. The orders were grouped into periods of increasingly enormous size—the first period ended with a number we would write as 1 followed by eight hundred million zeros, which, in turn, became the unit for the first order of the second period. This method could turn out numbers indefinitely. Archimedes developed it up to a number that we would have to express as 1 followed by eighty thousand million million zeros, which he demonstrated was more than adequate for counting the grains of all that hypothetical sand.

In modern mathematics we would count them in googols. If the word sounds as if it were made up by a child, it is because it was. Dr. Edward Kasner's nine-year-old nephew thought up the name, on request. Written out, it is:

10,000,000,000,000,000,000,000,000,000,000,000,000,
000,000,000,000,000,000,000,000,000,000,000,000,
000,000,000,000,000,000,000,000,000.

More compactly, it is expressed as 10^{100}. In this abbreviated notation the exponent tells you how many zeros you would have to put after the 1 if it were written the long way.

A googol is just about large enough to accommodate the largest numbers used in physics or astronomy. When the need arises for larger ones, mathematicians are ready with the googolplex (named by the same child). This is 1 followed by a googol of zeros. I couldn't write it out on this page, or in this entire book, nor on all the pages of all the books ever written. There wouldn't be room for all those zeros. In scientific notation it is $10^{10^{100}}$, which means to raise ten to the googolth power.

But no matter how big, these are just plain numbers, derived from counting—brothers and sisters of the ones on the conventional number line.

Using numbers of much more modest size, a number line is often used for teaching addition. If the problem is $2 + 3$, start at the left and count two spaces, then three more. There you are at five, the answer.

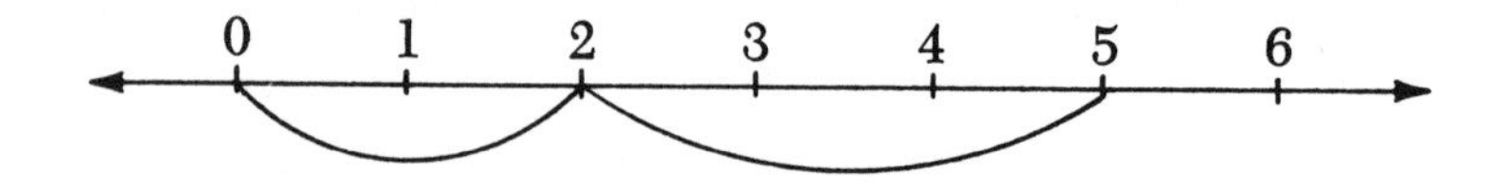

For subtraction, start at the right and work toward the left. To do $6 - 2$, start at 6, then count to the left two spaces and there is the answer at four.

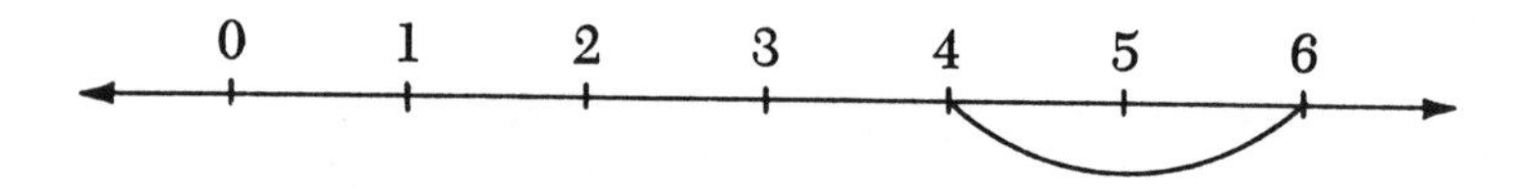

Multiplication, say 2×3, means to take two steps, each three spaces long, going from left to right.

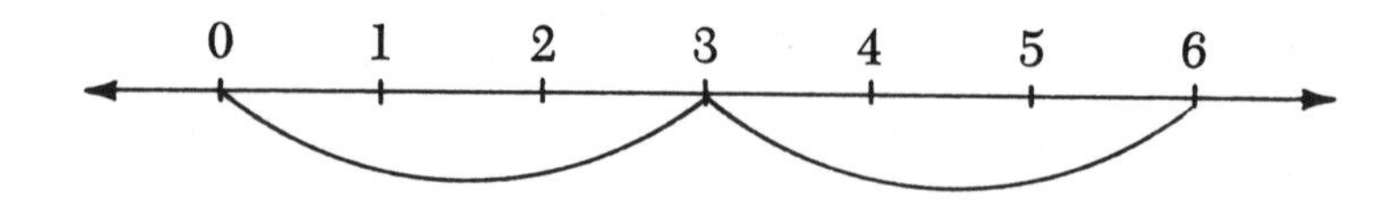

To illustrate $7 \div 2$, start at 7 and work toward the left, taking steps two spaces long until there isn't room for any more. The spaces left over are the remainder; the number of steps you took is the answer.

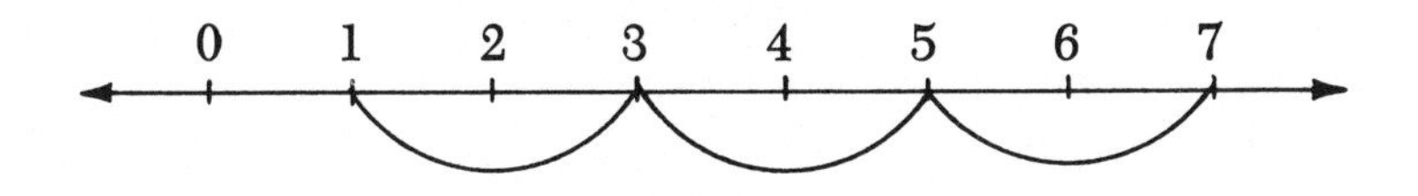

PROBLEMS

1. Which is larger, an octade or a googol?
2. Which is larger, a googol or the largest number developed by Archimedes?
3. Which is larger, a googolplex or the largest number developed by Archimedes?
4. Into which one of Archimedes' orders of the first period would a googol fit?

Rational Numbers

In the practical business of measuring, which consists of applying an arbitrary unit to an object and counting the number of times it is contained, the ancients could make do very well with the natural numbers as long as it came out even, but when it didn't—and it usually didn't—they were forced to employ fractions, a major step in the mathematics of antiquity.

At first they were handled very awkwardly. The Babylonians used only fractions whose denominator was 60; the Roman denominator was always 12. The Egyptians, on the other hand, didn't care what the denominator was, but insisted that the numerator had to be 1. Instead of $\frac{3}{4}$ they wrote the sum of $\frac{1}{2}$ and $\frac{1}{4}$. (The only exception they tolerated was $\frac{2}{3}$.) The Rhind papyrus, a sort of mathematical handbook called "Directions for Knowing All Dark Things," which was written by the Egyptian priest, Ahmes, seventeen hundred years before Christ, devotes a lot of space to a table showing division converted to this form. It wasn't easy—for instance, $2 \div 29$ had to be written as the sum of $\frac{1}{24}$, $\frac{1}{58}$, $\frac{1}{174}$, and $\frac{1}{232}$ instead of $\frac{2}{29}$, as we do. What made it so hard was that they did not use repetitions of the same fraction—each one had to be different.

It took centuries before the fractional numbers were accepted on an equal footing with the other numbers. For one thing, they don't have the same concrete character. The natural numbers stand like a row of columns, but if you try to fill the spaces between them with a picket fence of fractions you run into trouble, because a fractional number has no successor. If I ask what is the next whole number after 2, you say 3, but what's the next fractional number after $\frac{1}{2}$? What do you paint on that picket? There's no way to tell—the possibilities are infinite. Mathematicians call this property "density" and define it by saying that between any pair of fractional numbers another one can always be inserted, endlessly. It is hard to get a thought picture of a fence of fractions if you are always moving the pickets over and crowding in another one, closer and closer.

To be exact, what the mathematicians say is that between any two *rational* numbers another one can always be inserted, rational being the name given to the kinds of numbers we have mentioned so far because they can all be written as ratios: 2/3, or 64/25, or 3/1. If you try to draw a number line of the rational numbers, you are faced with a problem. Since there are infinitely many fractions between any two whole numbers, which ones are you going to put on the line? All you can do is write in a few as examples.

In the painful transition from the natural number system to the rational number system things will be easier if a student sees that all that has been changed is the unit of measurement. Mark a number line off all the way across in $\frac{1}{3}$'s. Then, if you disregard the denominators, you can add and subtract in exactly the same way as with whole numbers.

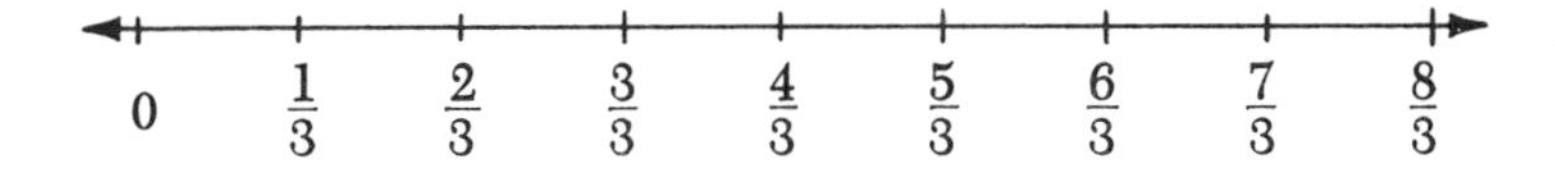

Even that old bugaboo, the common denominator, can be explained on the number line. Say you want to find the lowest common denominator for $\frac{1}{2}$, $\frac{1}{3}$, and $\frac{1}{4}$. Count by twos, by threes, and fours, until they all meet for the first time and that's it—12.

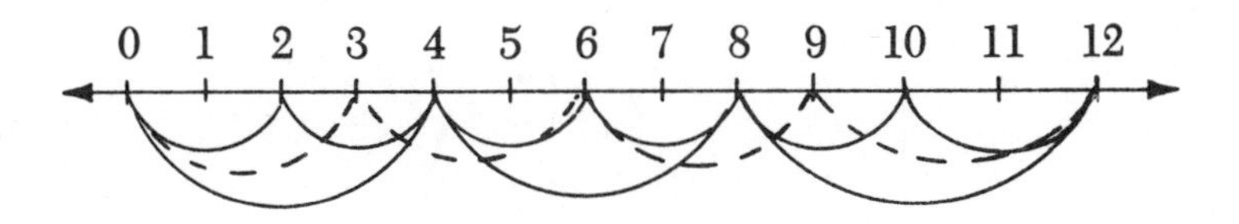

PROBLEMS

1. Write each of the following fractions in the Egyptian way: $\frac{5}{6}$; $\frac{3}{4}$; $\frac{5}{10}$; $\frac{5}{15}$; $\frac{2}{3}$.
2. Find the least common denominator of $\frac{1}{8}$, $\frac{2}{3}$, and $\frac{3}{4}$ by means of a number line.
3. Insert a rational number between $\frac{5}{16}$ and $\frac{7}{9}$. Now insert another rational number between that one and $\frac{5}{16}$.

Irrational Numbers

While it is true that there is a point on the number line for every rational number, the opposite does not hold—there is not a rational number for every point. In the preceding section, the number lines had only a few fractions put in as examples. You *could* fill in millions until the line was black with them, but even so, dense as the fractions may be, there are gaps in that line where no number in the rational system will fit. That is because there are things—the diagonals of some squares, for instance—that no rational number can measure exactly.

Construct a square with one unit as its side and draw the diagonal, then put the point of a compass on *A* and cut an arc. The distance along the line from *A* to *P* is the same length as the diagonal.

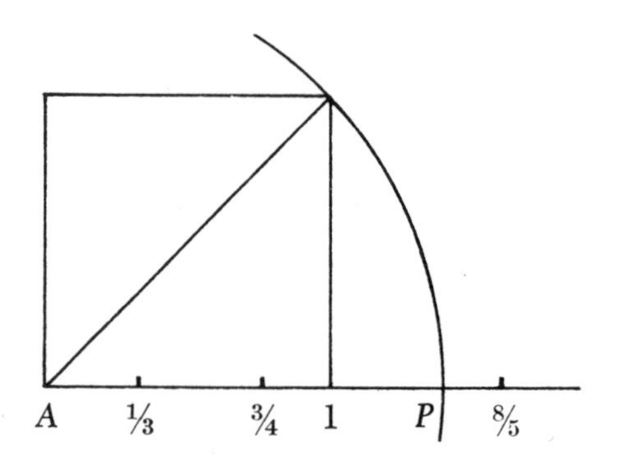

P may appear to fall on one of the rational numbers, but that is just because a construction can't be perfect—the width of the pencil mark covers a little space, while a point, technically, has no thickness. Actually, *P* is a point without a rational number. It cannot hit on one of the rationals because the length of the diagonal is irrational, a fact the Greeks discovered very early.

It was the Pythagoreans, a mystic brotherhood devoted to the study of mathematics and astronomy, who found this out when they were pursuing their famous theorem that the square on the hypotenuse of a right triangle is equivalent to the sum of the squares on the other two sides. You can see how it happened if you take the square you constructed and, since the diagonal divides it into two right triangles, apply their theorem as follows:

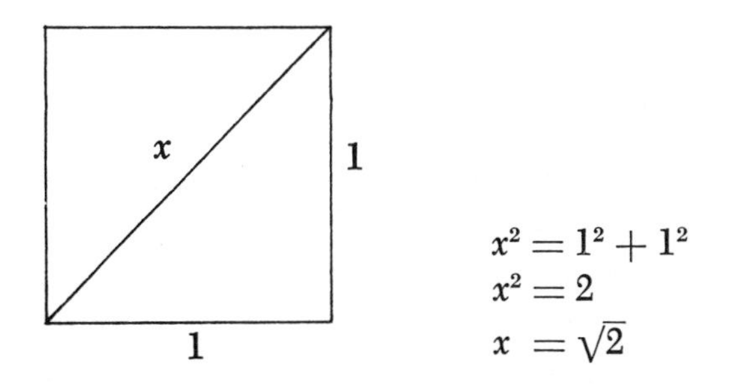

$$x^2 = 1^2 + 1^2$$
$$x^2 = 2$$
$$x = \sqrt{2}$$

But there is no rational number which multiplied by itself equals 2. If you look it up on a square-root table today and find 1.414, that is only an approximation, rounded off at the third decimal place. Square it and you get 1.999396, not 2. If you use a larger table you find $\sqrt{2}$ is 1.4142136, also an approximation. Give the problem to a computer and it will work until it wears itself out, if you don't turn it off. There is no number that is the square root of 2—no rational number, that is. Therefore it must be, by definition, irrational.

If you start the other way and call the diagonal 1, then the side comes out $\frac{1}{2}\sqrt{2}$, which is just as bad. There is simply something about that square which eludes the rational number system.

This discovery spread consternation among the Pythagoreans. Not only were they forced to scrap some of their mathematical theories, but it also struck at the heart of their philosophy. In their search for the world-stuff out of which everything else is created, they had come to hold the strange belief that "all things are numbers." Mixing a great deal of what we would call numerology with their mathematics, they had made a sort of religion out of the whole numbers. Yet here was a line that could be measured neither by a whole number nor a ratio of whole numbers.

The Greeks wrestled with the problem for years. They produced an airtight theoretical proof that $\sqrt{2}$ could not be rational. Theodorus of Cyrene, a Pythagorean who is said to have been Plato's teacher, discovered many more irrationals: $\sqrt{3}$, $\sqrt{5}$, $\sqrt{6}$, $\sqrt{7}$, $\sqrt{8}$, $\sqrt{10}$, $\sqrt{11}$, $\sqrt{12}$, $\sqrt{13}$, $\sqrt{14}$, $\sqrt{15}$, and $\sqrt{17}$.

Since the Greek numerals were merely the letters of their alphabet with no place value attached—α was one, β was two, etc.—they could not use decimal approximations, as we do. To try to evaluate such intractable numbers they hit upon the ingenious method of "the great and the small" which closed in on the irrationals from above and below.

First they constructed a ladder of numbers like this:

1	1
2	3
5	7
12	17
29	41
etc.	

The ratio of the two numbers on each rung comes nearer and nearer to the ratio $1/\sqrt{2}$. 2/3 is a little too small; 5/7 is a bit too large; 12/17 is again too small, but closer than 2/3.

As you go along the rungs of the ladder, the elusive ratio is caught in a sort of pincer movement.

The irrationals achieved status as bona-fide numbers when Plato, who was much influenced by the Pythagoreans, included them on an equal footing with the rationals in his lectures at the Academy. One of his pupils, the brilliant Eudoxus, put the theory of irrationals on such a sound logical basis that this masterpiece of ancient arithmetic was not equaled until the nineteenth century.

Today we sometimes use the number-within-a-nest method, which is similar to the Greek idea of squeezing the irrational from both sides, but expressed in our decimal notation and illustrated on a number line. You begin by thinking of the two nearest perfect squares. If the problem is to find the square root of 2, you see that it falls between $\sqrt{1}$, which is 1, and $\sqrt{4}$, which is 2. The first interval is that part of the number line between 1 and 2. Divide that into ten equal spaces. By squaring the endpoints of the most likely of those intervals, you find that $\sqrt{2}$ falls between 1.4 and 1.5 because 2 falls between the square of 1.4 and the square of 1.5. Divide *that* interval into ten parts, try those, and you see that it is between 1.41 and 1.42. As you keep this up, the size of the innermost of the nest of intervals keeps shrinking until, theoretically, every other number is eventually shut out, leaving $\sqrt{2}$ and nothing else.

Another approach is to consider all numbers as unending decimals. You are familiar with .333. . . for ⅓. (This is often written with a line over the 3 to show it repeats: $.\overline{3}$). In the same way ⅔ is $.\overline{6}$ and $\frac{1}{7}$ is $.\overline{142857}$, repeated over and over. By fudging a little and adding zeros, those that come out even such as ½ = .5, can be represented as repeating: ½ = $.5\overline{0}$. These are all rational numbers. When the irrationals are expressed as unending decimals, the difference is that they never repeat. Maybe one or two figures do, here and there, but there is no repetitive sequence, as in $1/7 = .\overline{142857}$. $\sqrt{2}$ is 1.4142136. . . , continued indefinitely, always different.

In such a way the irrational numbers were fitted into the domain of mathematics.

PROBLEMS

1. Discover the rule for selecting the numbers used on the Greeks' ladder and extend it three more rungs.
2. Convert each rung to a decimal fraction. Compare them with the decimal value of $1\sqrt{2}$. (For ease in computation this is the same as $\frac{1}{2}\sqrt{2}$.)
3. Extend the nest of intervals for the square root of 2 to the next three smaller. Compare their intervals with the decimal approximation of $\sqrt{2}$, given above.

Negative Numbers

Negative numbers, though simpler to understand, were not invented until long after the irrationals. Natural numbers are used when things are counted, fractions when things are measured, and irrational numbers are necessary for geometrical figures, but negative numbers do not occur naturally in relation to concrete objects. They are brought about by a property of number systems called closure. We say the natural numbers are closed under addition, which means that, if you add any two natural numbers, the answer is always a natural number. But this is true of subtraction only if you subtract the small number from the large one. If the natural numbers are the only ones at your disposal, a problem such as $3 - 5$ is impossible, meaning it is impossible in that number system. Extending the system to include fractions and irrationals does not help in subtracting 5 from 3. The system, as we have developed it so far, is not closed under subtraction.

The ancients did not solve this problem. Diophantus, one of the last of the Greeks, spoke of the "impossible solution of the absurd equation $4x + 16 = 4$"—a dead giveaway that he didn't have any negative numbers and therefore could not subtract 16 from 4. Today any first-year algebra student can find that $x = -3$.

The Greeks died, their great university at Alexandria fell to the Moors, and nothing of any great moment happened in Western mathematics for around a thousand years. The history of the subject passed to Arabia and India. There some unnamed genius invented the positional notation system—the way of writing numbers in Hindu-Arabic numerals that we are used to, including zero as a placeholder. (How could you tell 23 from 203 without a zero?) The idea of a number symbol, 0, for *none* was new to mankind. It is an unnatural number, calling for a certain amount of mathematical sophistication in order to understand all its properties—more sophistication than the ancient civilizations had, in fact.

Zero made it possible to subtract a number from its equal and have something to write for an answer. The next step was to find a way to take a large number from a smaller one —that way was the use of negatives. By the twelfth century, Bhaskara, a Hindu mathematician, wrote of solving a quadratic equation which came out $x = 50$ and $x = -5$. However, he remarked, "The second root is not to be taken, for it is inadequate. People do not approve of negative roots." They were still not psychologically ready for such an elastic concept of number.

The Hindu-Arabic notation and algebra were introduced into medieval Italy by Leonardo of Pisa (also called Fibonacci), who based his work on an Arabic treatise. He made one of the earliest attempts to give a concrete meaning to negative numbers by saying that in problems concerning profit, a negative answer meant a loss. This points up the basic idea necessary in extending the number line to include negatives—that of direction.

Algebra spread northward with the Renaissance. European mathematicians, like those in India, were dubious about negative numbers, using them when necessary but always with suspicion. They were not generally accepted until the seventeenth century. Even later, some diehards held out against the "strange doctrine of negative quantities," saying it was ruining the "otherwise clear and simple science of algebra."

When all these kinds of numbers are put together they make up the real number system. Shown on a number line it looks this way:

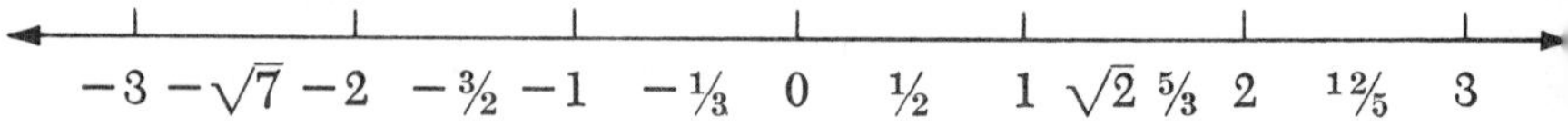

$-3 \quad -\sqrt{7} \quad -2 \quad -\frac{3}{2} \quad -1 \quad -\frac{1}{3} \quad 0 \quad \frac{1}{2} \quad 1 \quad \sqrt{2} \quad \frac{5}{3} \quad 2 \quad 1\frac{2}{5} \quad 3$

Zero is in the middle, the positive numbers to the right and the negatives to the left, running off in both directions as far as you like. Instead of a series of isolated points, it is continuous. There are no gaps. There is a number for every possible point and a point for every possible real number—

a one-to-one correspondence between the real number system and the points on the number line. To reach this happy state of affairs had taken several thousand years of human thought.

PROBLEMS

$$6,\ \tfrac{3}{4},\ \sqrt{5},\ 0,\ -12,\ 6\tfrac{1}{4},\ \sqrt{16},\ \sqrt{\tfrac{1}{4}},\ -5\tfrac{1}{2},\ -\sqrt{10},\ (\tfrac{1}{2}+\tfrac{1}{4}),\ (\tfrac{1}{4}-\tfrac{1}{2}),\ 5-\sqrt{3},\ 1.321\overline{56}$$

1. Which of the numbers in the list above are natural numbers?
2. Which are rational numbers but not natural numbers?
3. Which are both rational and natural?
4. Which are real but not rational?
5. Which are real and rational but not natural?

Complex Numbers

You think now with natural numbers, fractions, negatives, zero, and irrationals we are all set for any eventuality? Then suppose you try to solve the equation $x^2 = -9$. Now what? According to the law of signs, $(3)^2 = 9$ and $(-3)^2 = 9$, also. What squared makes -9? If you try to weasel out of it by saying 3 times -3, that's not squaring—the number has to be multiplied by *itself*. Here we go again. There isn't any real number whose square is negative, so obviously some unreal ones had to be invented, and they were—the imaginaries. Instead of being made of solid building blocks of 1's, they are constructed of units of *i*'s (for imaginary), and connected to the real numbers by the arbitrary definition that $i^2 = -1$. One answer to the problem above is $3i$. (Separate -9 into 9 times -1, then replace -1 by i^2. If $x = 3i$, then $x^2 = 9i^2$.)

If negative numbers were hard for people to swallow, imaginaries were ten times as bad. The Brahmin Bhaskara, in the twelfth century, outlawed answers such as $x = \sqrt{-9}$ by writing. "The square of a positive number, as also that of a negative number, is positive. There is no square root of a negative number, for a negative number is not a square." In the sixteenth century the Italian mathematician, Cardan, went so far as to write down $(5 + \sqrt{-15})\ (5 - \sqrt{-15})$ as the solution to a problem, but he made the reservation that it was meaningless, fictitious, and imaginary.

Such mathematical expressions kept occurring, to the point where they become as unavoidable as fractions and negatives. To achieve freedom in computation, the imaginary numbers had to be used and for the same reason that the fractions and decimals were—closure. The real number system is not closed under the operations performed in solving quadratic and cubic equations.

The name imaginary stuck, which is unfortunate, implying as it does something out of fairyland, supernatural and hallucinatory. They have many very real applications, especially in problems concerning alternating current electricity.

It is quite possible to start with concrete data, perform many and complicated mathematical manipulations, running into imaginary numbers along the way, and have the whole thing turn back into real numbers in the end. This is because of the following basic pattern:

$$
\begin{aligned}
i &= \sqrt{-1} \\
i^2 &= -1 \\
i^3 &= -1\,(i) \text{ or } -i \\
i^4 &= -1\,(-1) \text{ or } 1
\end{aligned}
$$

At alternate steps, beginning with the second, you are back in the real number system.

The hybrid form, such as $2 + 3i$, in which the roots of quadratic equations often appear is called a complex number—part real, part imaginary. The general form is $a + bi$. If $b = 0$, then the whole expression is merely a real number. If $a = 0$, then the number is a pure imaginary. Therefore all real numbers (including naturals, rationals, zero, negatives, and irrationals) as well as imaginaries are encompassed in the complex number system.

It takes a plane with *two* number lines to show all these kinds of numbers. The second one, for the imaginaries, is drawn perpendicular to the other. The two lines determine the complex plane on which any complex number can be represented by a point, as you see in the Argand diagram below (named for Monsieur Argand, a Parisian bookkeeper who was one of three people to invent it at about the same time—i.e., the nineteenth century).

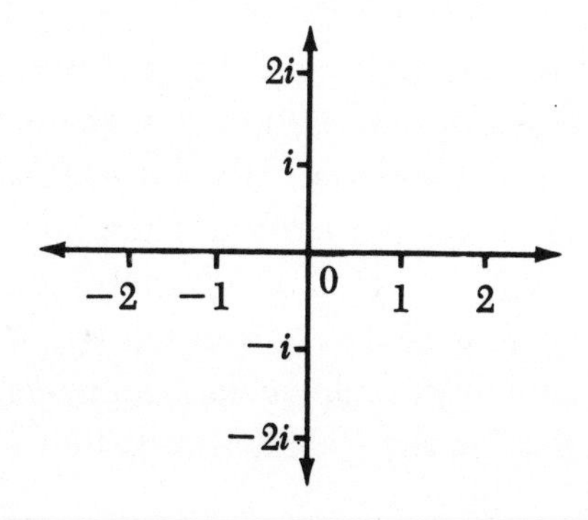

In the new mathematics a complex number is treated as an ordered pair of real numbers (a, b). This viewpoint is summarized in the *Principles of Mathematics* by Allendoerfer and Oakley: "For historical reasons, a is called the real part of $a + bi$ and b is called its imaginary part. No significance is attached to these words; they are mere labels denoting 'first' and 'second' member of the pair (a, b)."

PROBLEMS

1. Which of the following are actually real numbers in disguise? $i, i^2, 3i^3, i^6, -i^4, 2i^8, -5i$
2. Treating i as any letter in algebra, multiply $2 + 3i$ by $2 - 3i$. Is your answer a real or imaginary number?

The mathematics curriculum in the schools now includes a systematic study of the number system because of a general trend on the part of mathematicians to tidy up and streamline what is, historically, a rather jerry-built edifice. It has been nailed together over the centuries as the need arose, with here a suite for the integers, there a mezzanine for the fractions, and yonder an attic for irrational numbers. Part of the architecture is Moorish. There are cupolas and spires and minarets, connected by labyrinthine corridors and stairways and elevator shafts. At the top is a mooring mast tethering a dirigible full of imaginary numbers—units of i's that are as ethereal as the gas-filled cells that kept the zeppelins afloat.

The logical development of the various number systems, as shown by the following chart, is slightly different from the historical order.

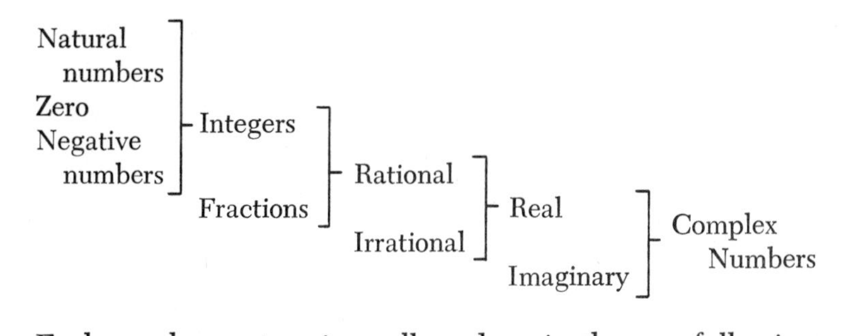

Each number system is swallowed up in the one following it. Using set symbolism (see chapter on sets, section on subsets), the relationship between the sets of numbers would be:

Natural numbers $\subset$ Integers $\subset$ Rational $\subset$ Real $\subset$ Complex Numbers

You might think that this process of extension would have to go on indefinitely, but that is not the case. Start with complex numbers, perform any algebraic operations you want to with them, and, praises be, the answer is always another complex number. In other words, the set of complex numbers is closed under all algebraic operations, except for dividing by 0 and 0^0.

We had to give up something to achieve this though—the property of order. Since the complex numbers correspond to points scattered over a plane, instead of being marshaled along a straight line like the reals, it is impossible to say whether $3 + 4i$ is greater than, equal to, or smaller than $4 + 3i$.

5

Other Number Systems—Two-Fingered Machines and Sixteen-Fingered Martians

Not only do the computers perform their intricate calculations in the twinkling of an eye, but most of the machines do them in a number system different from the one the rest of us use. They do not merely provide a faster way of doing the old math, as you might think, but demand different subject matter.

Since an electric switch has just two choices—on or off—computers represent numbers by using only two symbols, 1 (on) and 0 (off), instead of the 0,1,2,3,4,5,6,7,8,9 that we are used to. Such a binary, or base two, system isn't new. It has been around a long time, but was regarded as a sort of mathematical curiosity until the advent of the computers.

Binary Arithmetic

In the binary system "110" doesn't mean one hundred and ten—it means six. You do this by changing the invisible headings that we have been schooled to see over each digit. Instead of:

Hundreds	Tens	Units
1	1	0

it becomes:

Fours	Twos	Units
1	1	0

In other words, 1 four, 1 two, and no units—they add up to six. Each heading is twice the one to the right, instead of ten times it. In this way any number, no matter how large, can be expressed by just two symbols.

Sixty-fours	Thirty-twos	Sixteens	Eights	Fours	Twos	Units
1	1	0	1	0	1	1

Add them up and you get one hundred and seven. This may be cumbersome for us, but it's convenient for the machines, and, brother, that's what counts.

Those who work with computers call the binary digits "bits." Professor Franklin McFeely, in an article in the May, 1959, *Mathematics Teacher* called, "One Plus One Equals Toon," suggests regular names for the numbers in the binary system, Toon, written 10, is two, three is etooven (11), four (100) is toodred, etc. These names have not caught on, but you do need something to call 10—you have to fight the temptation to say "ten." The best we can do at present is to read it "one zero," or "one two and zero."

To understand addition in binary arithmetic, think of the numbers as rows of light bulbs, each individual bulb turned on for 1, off for 0. Then picture a row of bulbs for the answer, each one wired to the ones in the column above it in such a way that it flashes on or off according to the sum of the digits in that column.

$$\begin{array}{r} 110 \\ +101 \\ \hline 1011 \end{array} \qquad \text{Check:} \quad \begin{array}{r} 6 \\ +5 \\ \hline 11 \end{array}$$

Starting at the right, $1 + 0 = 1$, so that light comes on in the answer. The same is true in the second column. But in the third one, $1 + 1$ is more than one. Some other arrangement has to be made. It is handled by having that bulb go off and the one in the column to the left flash on—in other words, a mechanism for carrying one. The problem is checked by converting it to ordinary arithmetic.

The addition table is as follows:

+	0	1
0	0	1
1	1	10

Use it to solve this problem:

$$\begin{array}{r} 10111 \\ +1010 \\ \hline 100001 \end{array} \qquad \text{Check:} \quad \begin{array}{r} 23 \\ +10 \\ \hline 33 \end{array}$$

The multiplication table is easier:

×	0	1
0	0	0
1	0	1

Multiplying by a single digit is child's play—the answer is always either identical with the first number, or it is zero.

$$\begin{array}{r} 10110 \\ \times \quad 1 \\ \hline 10110 \end{array} \qquad \text{Check:} \quad \begin{array}{r} 22 \\ \times\ 1 \\ \hline 22 \end{array}$$

$$\begin{array}{r} 10110 \\ \times \quad 0 \\ \hline 00000 \end{array} \qquad \text{Check:} \quad \begin{array}{r} 22 \\ \times\ 0 \\ \hline 0 \end{array}$$

When a two-digit multiplier is used, the problem is harder, since addition is involved.

$$\begin{array}{r} 10110 \\ \times \quad 11 \\ \hline 10110 \\ 10110 \\ \hline 1000010 \end{array} \qquad \text{Check:} \quad \begin{array}{r} 22 \\ \times\ 3 \\ \hline 66 \end{array}$$

Although the binary system has a practical application in computer mathematics, this is only a secondary reason for introducing it into the school curriculum. The primary purpose is to give insight into the workings and structure of ordinary, base ten, arithmetic. The decimal system is so familiar that the reasons underlying its operations are often overlooked, but handling a strange system affords an opportunity for the discovery of these reasons, which are common to all number systems.

PROBLEMS

Change each of the following binary numerals to their equivalent in the ordinary, base ten, system:

1. 1100
2. 1010
3. 111
4. 110011
5. 1111100

Assuming that the following are numerals in the base two system, perform the indicated computations in binary arithmetic:

6. $111 + 101$
7. $1101 + 1111$
8. 1011×10
9. 111001×111
10. $110\,(11011 + 1011)$

Other Bases

For convenience in working with computers, bits are often divided into groups of three. In that case the headings are fours, twos, and units, repeated over and over. Since four + two + one is seven, each trio of bits can express any number from 0 through 7:

fours	twos	units	fours	twos	units	fours	twos	units
1	1	0	0	1	1	1	0	1
	6			3			5	

But this is not six hundred and thirty-five. We are now using eight symbols—0,1,2,3,4,5,6,7—which means that we are in a number system with a base of eight, the octal system. Its headings are:

Sixty-fours	Eights	Units
6	3	5

Worked out: $6(64) + 3(8) + 5(1)$ equals 413 in the ordinary, or base ten, system.

Some computers work in base eight, but you do not have to confine your study of number systems to those that have practical applications. Once you get used to this free-wheeling idea, you can make up a number system using any base you want to.

The Babylonians used a base of sixty, the Mayas of Yucatán calculated in base twenty. The Duodecimal Society of America has, for a number of years, been trying to get the United States to change over to a base of twelve, on the grounds that twelve makes computation easier since it is divisible by two, three, four, and six, and that it is more compatible with many of our common measures—twelve things in a dozen, twelve inches in a foot, three feet in a yard, etc.

The only reason most civilizations have used ten is that humans happen to have ten fingers. If it should turn out that the Martians have sixteen, then the astronauts will probably find them using a system based on sixteen.

If you would like to compute in such a pseudo-Martian system, you need sixteen number symbols. Since we have only ten, you will have to piece out with letters: 0,1,2,3,4,5, 6,7,8,9,a,b,c,d,e,f, where a = ten, b = eleven, c = twelve, d = thirteen, e = fourteen, f = fifteen. Here is an addition problem:

Sixteen sixteens (Two hundred fifty-six)	Sixteens	Units	
1	5	b	(This is 347, earth style)
3	c	8	(968)
5	2	3	(1315)

It is done exactly the same way as in the decimal system. Beginning on the right:

Units	
b	(i.e., 11)
8	
19	

Take sixteen units out, roll them together into 1 sixteen, and carry it to the next column, leaving 3 units

Sixteens	
1	(carried)
5	
c	(i.e., 12)
18	

Take sixteen of these sixteens out, bundle them up into 1 two hundred fifty-six, and carry it to the next column, leaving 2 of them behind.

Two hundred fifty-six
1 (carried)
1
3
―
5

You can see the necessity for indicating which base is being used. Otherwise there would be a mathematical Tower of Babel, with everybody calculating in a different system. It is customary to write the base as a subscript to the right of the last figure—635_{eight}, 413_{ten}, or 110011101_{two}. (These are all really the same number—work them out and see.) There is a technical reason for writing the subscripts in words instead of numerals. The octal system has no symbol for eight, therefore it would not be correct to write 635_8. The same is true for every system—there is no symbol 2 in the binary system, no symbol 5 in the quinary system, no 16 in the base sixteen system. Many textbooks, as a practical matter of convenience, however, do write 635_8 and all the other bases in a similar way. It's a sort of gentlemen's agreement, to save time, although the gentlemen all know it is not technically accurate to do so.

You also need some way of changing numbers from one system to another. The method of converting from a different base into base ten has already been indicated above—just multiply each digit by the heading of its column and add all the results. To go the other way—from base ten to a new system—there is a handy algorithm that does the trick. ("Algorithm" is an old-fashioned word, meaning a step-by-step procedure, which has come back into style because computers require step-by-step procedures.) This is the remainder method. Start with the number in base ten and divide over and over by the new base, writing down the remainders each time. Then list the remainders *in reverse order* and there is the number in the new base. For example, to convert 23_{ten} to the binary system:

2) 23
2) 11 Remainder 1
2) 5 Remainder 1
2) 2 Remainder 1
2) 1 Remainder 0
0 Remainder 1

$10111_{two} = 23_{ten}$

That same number—23_{ten}—changed to base five would be:

5) 23
5) 4 Remainder 3
0 Remainder 4

$43_{five} = 23_{ten}$

Notice that the smaller the base, the longer the number turns out to be, which is logical, since you have fewer symbols at your disposal and have to repeat them over and over to express any given number.

It is difficult to change directly from one of these exotic systems to another without going through base ten first, since the calculating would have to be done in one of the strange systems. If you want to change 32_{five} to base seven, it is easier to first convert to the equivalent in base ten, and then go to base seven, doing all the computing in the good old decimal system.

The exception (among the systems we have discussed)

is in changing back and forth between the binary and the octal system. Since the cube of 2 (the base of one system) equals 8 (the base of the other), the numerals can be converted directly by grouping, as explained at the beginning of this section.

PROBLEMS

Change each of the following to equivalent decimal numerals:

1. 125_{eight}
2. $29_{sixteen}$
3. 312_{five}
4. 910_{twelve}

Change each of the following decimal numerals to the indicated base:

5. 93 to base five
6. 45 to base two
7. 173 to base twelve
8. 105 to base two
9. Change 110010101_{two} to the octal numeration system.
10. Change 213_{five} to the binary numeration system.

Modular Arithmetic

There is still another kind of number system, different from those we have described—the modulo system. A modulus is a sort of deuces-wild device that shakes arithmetic out of its old-time rigidity. It can be any number—a clock works on a modulo twelve system. If it's ten o'clock now and you add four hours, it is then two, not fourteen, o'clock. After each circuit of twelve hours, it starts over. The ordinary sum—14—is reduced by 12, which is called the modulus.

There is a mathematical symbol—a third bar in the equals sign—that is a warning that the calculation is in a foreign language, so to speak. Technically, the problem about the clock should be written $10 + 4 \equiv 2 \pmod{12}$ and read: "$10 + 4$ is congruent to 2, modulo 12."

Nobody intends for this modular, or clock, arithmetic to replace the ordinary kind. (In fact, it cannot.) You are not going to be able to buy a ten-dollar pair of sneakers and a four-dollar record album and pay only two dollars. It is, rather, a simplified model—a closed-in, limited system, with no fractions, no big numbers, and no negatives.

Draw a clock face with only five hours on it and you are ready for modulo five arithmetic.

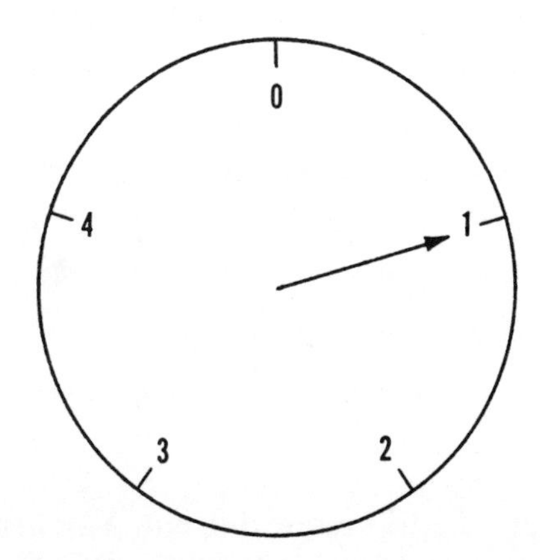

Count to three, then add four more spaces and you are at 2. So $3 + 4 \equiv 2$. You can count the other examples out the same way. Notice there is no number for five—you are just back at zero again. Problems in the modulo five system use only the figures 0,1,2,3,4. You can do any amount of addition of these numbers by counting around and around. The answer is never more than four. It can't be—this system has no higher numbers. If you get tired counting, make yourself an addition table like this:

+	0	1	2	3	4
0	0	1	2	3	4
1	1	2	3	4	0
2	2	3	4	0	1
3	3	4	0	1	2
4	4	0	1	2	3

Multiplication is done the way little children and machines do—by repeated additions. 2×3 means to count two spaces, then two more, then again two more, making three times. It comes out 1. Here is the multiplication table:

$\times$	0	1	2	3	4
0	0	0	0	0	0
1	0	1	2	3	4
2	0	2	4	1	3
3	0	3	1	4	2
4	0	4	3	2	1

Equations are a little more difficult. For instance, in the problem $x + 4 = 2$. You can't transpose—there aren't any negative numbers in a modulo system, since the clock always moves forward. You have to think of a number that would make a zero on the left side of the equation. What added to 4 makes 0? As you see from the addition table, it has to be a 1, so add 1 to both sides:

$$x + 4 + 1 \equiv 2 + 1$$
$$x + 0 \equiv 3$$
$$x \equiv 3$$

Check: $3 + 4 \equiv 2$
$2 \equiv 2$

Try a harder problem: $3x + 1 \equiv 3$. First you have to add 4 in order to make a zero:

$$3x + 1 + 4 \equiv 3 + 4$$
$$3x + 0 \equiv 2$$
$$3x \equiv 2$$

Now what to multiply $3x$ by to make $1x$? It takes a 2, so multiply each side:

$$2\,(3x) \equiv 2\,(2)$$
$$1x \equiv 4$$
$$x \equiv 4$$

Check: $3\,(4) + 1 \equiv 3$
$2 + 1 \equiv 3$
$3 \equiv 3$

You probably have figured out by this time that you really don't need a table for the checks at all. Just do the problem in ordinary arithmetic, divide by five, and use only the remainder. It is a little like the method of tallying that everybody knows where the fifth mark goes through the first four: 𝍸 || . If you disregard the completed bundles and look only at the number of marks in the last group, that is the same as the answer in a modulo five system.

Two numbers are said to be congruent, modulo five, if they have the same remainder when divided by 5. In the check of the problem above, 13 is congruent to 3. Tallied, 13 is 𝍸 𝍸 ||| ; 3 is ||| . The unfinished bundles each have three marks in them, therefore the numbers are congruent. So are all numbers that come out that same way—8, 𝍸 | | | ; 18, 𝍸 𝍸 𝍸 | | | ; etc. They are also said to belong to the same residue class—residue being what is left over after the groups of five are taken out. 3, 8, 13, and 18 all belong to the 3 class, modulo five. 7 and 12 are in the 2 class, modulo five, because they each have two marks left in the unfinished bundle. That is, they leave a remainder of 2 when divided by 5.

PROBLEMS

Perform the following computations in the modulo 5 number system:

1. $1 + 2 + 3$
2. $2 + 4 + 2 + 1$
3. $2\,(3)$
4. $3\,(3)(4)$

Solve the following equations in the modulo 5 system:

5. $x + 4 \equiv 0$
6. $3x \equiv 2$
7. $2x + 1 \equiv 3$
8. Find three integers congruent to 4, mod 5.
9. Find three integers that are in the 1 class, mod 5.
10. Find an integer x which satisfies: $x + 3 \equiv 2$, mod 5.

Modulo Ten System

There is nothing special about using five as the modulus—any number will do. A modulo ten system will bring out the similarities to regular arithmetic. Make a clock with ten spaces:

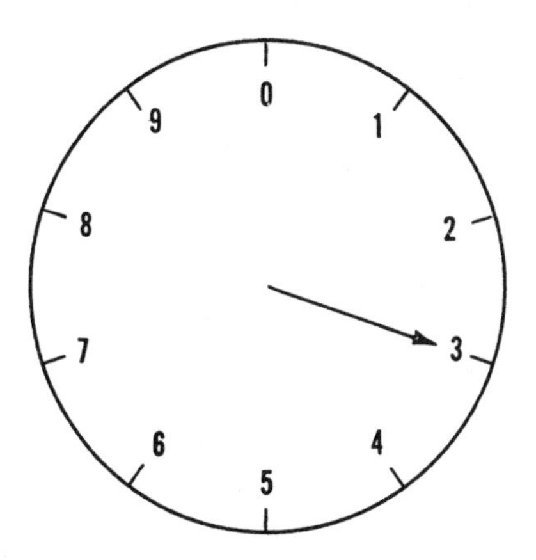

Then $3 + 4 = 7$, $4 + 5 = 9$, and everything looks natural as long as the answer has only one figure. But $6 + 8 = 4$, and $9 + 9 = 8$, because we are dropping off the first figure and writing down only the last one. We are not counting the number of times the hand has gone around—only where it stops. Since that is the case, there is no carrying in modulo ten arithmetic.

By keeping track of the number of times the hand has circled the clock, it is easily converted into ordinary arithmetic. $6 + 8 = 14$, because the hand has gone around once and is now at four. Such an approach helps you to understand where all the rules about carrying and borrowing come from. The idea is to discover the structure, not memorize a set of rules.

Without this understanding, some people do arithmetic like a color-blind man in a jelly-bean factory trying to sort out the green ones from the red ones. Unable to see the color—the crux of the matter—he has to look for something else to guide him. Maybe the reds are a little blunter at the end, or a trifle smaller. Maybe they smell different. As a last resort he might lick them and separate the peppermint from the wintergreen by taste. In the same way many look for something tangible to hang on to, such as: "In division, always invert the second fraction," and memorize it. This works fine as long as the problems are all alike and there is just one rule, but when the rules pile up to ten or fifteen, that kind of method breaks down. Like the jelly-bean worker, he makes more mistakes and is considerably slower than one who sees the point.

PROBLEMS

Perform the following computations in the modulo ten system:

1. $6 + 7 + 5$
2. $3(7)$
3. $9 + 5 + 6(3)$
4. Construct an addition table for a modulo seven system.
5. Construct a multiplication table for a modulo three system.
6. Find three integers congruent to 5, mod 7.

Solve the following equations in the modulo ten system:

7. $x + 9 = 1$
8. $7x = 4$

Modulo Six System

One property of our ordinary arithmetic that is often hazily understood is this: If the product of two numbers is zero, one of them has to be zero. This is not true in every modulo system. Make a clock and a multiplication table using six as a modulus:

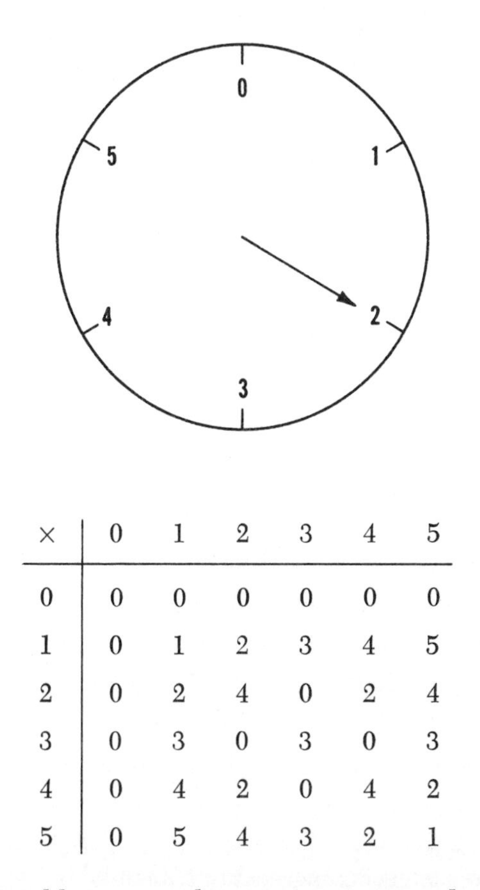

×	0	1	2	3	4	5
0	0	0	0	0	0	0
1	0	1	2	3	4	5
2	0	2	4	0	2	4
3	0	3	0	3	0	3
4	0	4	2	0	4	2
5	0	5	4	3	2	1

From the table you see that 2 times 3 is 0, and so is 4 times 3. You cannot find a single example on a standard multiplication table where two numbers, neither of which is zero, multiply together to equal zero.

Go back and look at the multiplication table for the modulo five system. In every case where the product is zero, one of the factors is zero. It behaves like ordinary arithmetic, in this respect.

Why the difference? Because five is a prime number and six is not. Two times three equals six, and six is replaced by zero in the table. The same is true of four times three because twelve, a multiple of six, is also replaced by zero.

This property (if the product of two numbers is zero, one of them must be zero) is basic in the solution of equations. Since the modulo six system lacks it, equations solved in this system come out strangely. $2x = 4$ has two perfectly good answers: $x = 2$ and $x = 5$. (Ordinarily, an equation has no more solutions than its degree—that is, a first-degree equation, which this is, could have only one.) On the other hand, $2x = 3$ has no solution at all. Look on the table under the column headed 2 and you will see that it is impossible to get a 3, no matter what you multiply by.

PROBLEMS

Solve the following equations in the modulo six system:

1. $2x = 2$
2. $4x = 2$
3. $4 = 5x$

Perform the following computations in the modulo six system:

4. $5 + 4 + 3$
5. $4 + 4 + 3(5)$
6. Find three integers congruent to 2, modulo six.

6

Properties of Number Systems—The Bones of Mathematics

In your math book you probably see references to the ACD laws—association, commutation, and distribution. The principles contained in these laws are already familiar to you. You use them, without realizing it, whenever you add, subtract, multiply, or divide.

They are in the textbooks because of the current emphasis on deductive proof. Since mathematics is man-made, it is not infallible. There have been times in the past when cracks have appeared in the structure—notably the Pythagoreans' discovery of the irrationality of $\sqrt{2}$, referred to in Chapter Four—because part of it was based only on what is usually called common sense. Therefore, a rigorous proof is necessary for each new invention. This is part of the trend away from physical reality and toward abstract theory which is a characteristic of modern mathematics.

In the long history of man's attempts at problem solving the pendulum has swung back and forth between empirical and theoretical methods. The empiricists collect a number of examples, tabulate the results, and then make what amounts to an informed guess about the answer to all similar problems. It is never absolutely certain, but only *probably* correct. Their method is composed of trial, error, intuition, and legwork. The theorist, on the other hand, lies back in a hammock and deduces truths from certain basic postulates by a chain of pure logic which proves it for every case, without exception.

The Babylonians and Egyptians used empirical means exclusively, and they discovered a great deal of elementary mathematical truth by collecting myriads of examples over long periods of time. The theoretical method originated in Greece, where it came to full flower in Euclid's Elements about 300 B.C. It is the method used in geometry, which begins with certain terms, definitions, and postulates, then from these are deduced a chain of theorems. After the decline of Greek civilization it languished, and the empirical and practical prevailed for nearly two thousand years. But in the nineteenth century there began to be a revival of the classical ideal of precision and rigorous proof. Once more the tide turned toward logical purity and abstraction. We are now well into that period—the so-called modern mathematical method is the same deductive-postulational approach of the Greeks.

In keeping with this ideal, arithmetic and algebra are now organized into a theoretical structure like geometry. Such a Euclidean method calls for the setting down at the beginning of a few assertions that are assumed without proof, and then deducing everything else from them. The ACD laws are these assertions. They play the same role that the postulates, such as "All right angles are equal" and "Only one straight line can be drawn through two given points," do in geometry.

The ACD Laws and Arithmetic

The simplest of these, stated in mathematical language, is the commutative property for addition: $a + b = b + a$. In other words, the sum of two numbers is not affected by the order in which they are added. For example: $5 + 1 = 1 + 5$. The commutative property for multiplication is $ab = ba$, or $3(4) = 4(3)$.

The law of association declares an equally obvious fact—that $2 + (3 + 4) = (2 + 3) + 4$. (Do the part in parentheses first and then add the other number.) Formally stated, the associative property for addition: $a + (b + c) = (a + b) + c$. It is necessary because addition is a binary operation—only two can take part in it at a time. To add three numbers, you first add any two of them, then add that answer to the third one. The law of association merely states what you already know—that it doesn't matter which two you add first.

As you probably surmised, there is also a law of association for multiplication. $(a \times b) \times c = a \times (b \times c)$. Changing partners does not affect the outcome, as you can tell by working out $(2 \times 3) \times 4$ and $2 \times (3 \times 4)$.

The D in ACD stands for the law of distribution. You need this in problems where both addition and multiplication are involved. Formally stated, the distributive property is: $a \times (b + c) = (a \times b) + (a \times c)$. That is, 4 times $(2 + 3) = 4(2) + 4(3)$. Add 2 and 3, then multiply the answer by 4, and it's the same as multiplying each number separately by 4 and then adding.

Any time you multiply by a two-digit number, you are using the law of distribution, although the traditional way of writing it somewhat conceals the fact.

$$\begin{array}{r} 23 \\ \times\ 12 \\ \hline 46 \\ 23 \\ \hline 276 \end{array}$$

What you did was to take 2 times 23, making 46, a partial product, then 10 times 23, giving 230, the other partial product, and then add the two partial products. We move the "23" over one space to the left, showing there is really a zero after the "3," although it is invisible.

PROBLEMS

Which of the following statements are true: For those which are true, name the law involved:

1. $(3 + 2) + 5 = (2 + 3) + 5$
2. $4 + (3 \times 5) = (4 + 3) \times (4 + 5)$
3. $4 + (3 + 1) = (4 + 3) + 1$
4. $8 \times 3 = 3 \times 8$
5. $4 - 6 = 6 - 4$
6. $3 \times (6 + 5) = (3 \times 6) + 5$
7. $2 \times (4 \times 6) = (2 \times 4) \times 6$
8. $6(2 + 5) = [6(2)] + [6(5)]$
9. $(12 \div 3) \div 2 = 3 \div (12 \div 2)$
10. $(9 + 14) \times (23 + 5) = [(9 + 14) \times 23] + [(9 + 14) \times 5]$

Other Number Properties

Closure has already been mentioned in the chapter on number systems. It is, simply, the property of remaining closed, which a given set of numbers may (or may not) possess when a certain operation is performed on some of its members. For instance, the set of whole numbers is closed under addition. Add any two whole numbers and the answer is again a whole number—a member of the original set. The same is true of multiplication, but if you divide you may get a fraction, as in $2 \div 7$. $2/7$ is not a member of the set of whole numbers—it is an outsider. Therefore, the set of whole numbers possesses the property of closure under addition or multiplication, but not under division.

Zero and one have special properties which the other numbers lack. Zero is the identity element for addition—add it to any number and the sum is that same number. In symbols, $a + 0 = a$. 1 serves the same purpose in multiplication—multiply any number by 1 and the answer is the original number, that is, $a \times 1 = a$.

The existence of these identity elements gives meaning to the idea of an inverse. -2 is the additive inverse of 2 because their sum is 0. This leads to the concept of subtraction as the inverse operation to addition. One undoes the other. Instead of subtracting, the same result can be obtained by adding the inverse element. For example, $6 + (-2)$ is exactly the same as subtracting 2 from 6. Therefore the idea of subtraction as a separate operation can be done away with entirely.

In the same way the multiplicative inverse of a number is that number by which you can multiply it to make 1. The multiplicative inverse of 5 is $1/5$, because their product is 1. The other name for it is "reciprocal." Every rational number, except 0, has exactly one reciprocal, which you can find by turning its fraction upside down. $4/3$ is the reciprocal of $3/4$, and vice versa.

Division is the inverse operation to multiplication. You

actually use it to answer the question "By what must I multiply?" In a divsion problem you are given one factor and the product—you have to find the other factor. You can do this by multiplying by the reciprocal. In fact, you are accustomed to doing this with fractions, because of the old rule "To divide by a fraction, invert and multiply." In the problem $4/5 \div 2/3$ you automatically put $4/5 \times 3/2$ and come out with $12/10$ or $1\frac{1}{5}$. But why?

$4/5 \div 2/3$ really means $2/3 \times ? = 4/5$. To find the ?, you could reason as follows, with one of the ACD laws or number properties to back you up at every step:

$1 \times 4/5 = 4/5$ (1 is the multiplicative identity)
$2/3 \times 3/2 = 1$ (multiplicative inverse)

Therefore you can substitute $(2/3 \times 3/2)$ for the 1 in the first equation and you have:

$(2/3 \times 3/2) \times 4/5 = 4/5$
$2/3 \times (3/2 \times 4/5) = 4/5$ (Law of Association for Multiplication)

This is just like $2/3 \times ? = 4/5$, with ? replaced by $(3/2 \times 4/5)$. When you find out what $3/2 \times 4/5$ is, you will have found the number that must replace the ?.

Looking at it this way, we can get rid of division as an operation in its own right, since to divide by a number you can always multiply by its reciprocal. $12 \div 4$ is the same as $12 \times 1/4$. This leaves only two basic operations— addition and multiplication. They possess the commutative and associative properties while the inverse operations—subtraction and division—do not. $6 - 2$ is not the same as $2 - 6$. Neither is $6 \div 2$ the same as $2 \div 6$. $(5 - 3) - 2$ does not equal

$5 - (3 - 2)$, either, nor does $(6 \div 2) \div 3$ equal $6 \div (2 \div 3)$.

When all the layers of flash cards and drill books are scraped away and the underlying mathematical bones of arithmetic exposed, you will see that they consist of the following:

Closure Law for Addition
Closure Law for Multiplication
Commutative Law for Addition
Commutative Law for Multiplication
Associative Law for Addition
Associative Law for Multiplication
Identity Law for Addition
Identity Law for Multiplication
Inverse Law for Addition
Inverse Law for Multiplication
Distributive Law

These eleven laws form the foundation of the entire subject of arithmetic.

PROBLEMS

1. Give the additive inverse of each of the following: 3, $\frac{1}{2}$, 1, -2, $-\frac{4}{3}$
2. Give the multiplicative inverse of each number in problem 1.

Name the law that is illustrated by each of the following:

3. $6 \times \frac{1}{6} = 1$
4. $5 + 0 = 5$
5. $3 + (-3) = 0$
6. $4 \times 1 = 4$

The ACD and Other Laws in Algebra

Algebra is now taught as a study of the structure of a mathematical system, rather than a kind of symbolized arithmetic using letters instead of numbers, which was the old way. Proof plays a large part in today's algebra course. The central idea in a logical structure, in the mathematical sense, is that some statements are consequences of other statements. This is succinctly called "if-then thinking." To prove a statement that is in the form "If A, then B" you have to construct a chain of reasons leading from A to B, and the reasons must be chosen from the basic properties of the system.

The eleven laws listed for arithmetic also hold for algebra. Add to these a few axioms such as "A quantity may be substituted for its equal in any expression without changing the value of the expression" (in the more precise language of today, "The name for any number may be replaced by any other name for the same number without affecting the meaning"), or "If the same quantity is added to equal quantities, the sums are equal" and you are equipped to prove a few theorems in algebra. It is not a proof, of course, if there is a loophole in it—every step must be legal. Try this:

To prove: $(a - b) + b = a$
Proof:

$(a - b) + b = [a + (-b)] + b = a + (-b + b)$ Law of Association

$-b + b = 0$ Additive inverse

$(a - b) + b = a + 0$ Substitution

$(a - b) + b = a$ Additive identity

Or this:

To prove: $(a + b)(c + d) = ac + bc + ad + bd$
Proof:

$(a + b)(c + d) = [(a + b)c] + [(a + b)d]$ Law of Distribution
$= [c(a + b)] + [d(a + b)]$ Commutative property of multiplication
$= [(ca) + (cb)] + [(da) + (db)]$ Law of Distribution
$= [(ac) + (bc)] + [(ad) + (bd)]$ Commutative property of multiplication
$= [(ac) + (bc) + (ad)] + (bd)$ Associative property of addition
$= (ac) + (bc) + (ad) + (bd)$ or
$= ac + bc + ad + bd$ Convention of performing multiplication before addition

A problem involving the two negative signs is trickier:

To prove: $-(-a) = a$
Proof: $-a$ exists Additive inverse

$-(-a) + (-a) = 0$ Additive inverse
$[-(-a) + (-a)] + a = 0 + a$ Addition axiom
$[-(-a) + (-a)] + a = a$ Identity element in addition
$-(-a) + [(-a) + a] = a$ Law of Association for addition
$[(-a) + a] = 0$ Additive inverse
$-(-a) + 0 = a$ Substitution
$-(-a) = a$ Identity element in addition

PROBLEMS

1. Prove that $(2a + 3b) + (5a + 7b) = 7a + 10b$
2. Prove that $ab + ac + ad = a(b + c + d)$
3. Prove that $(a + 2b)(2a + b) = 2a^2 + 5ab + 2b^2$

Mathematical Systems

What is a mathematical system? It is a set of objects together with one or more operations which can be performed on them. A table really describes a mathematical system. If you study an ordinary multiplication table—say the fives—it tells you many things besides the answer to 5 times 5.

×	1	2	3	4	5
1	1	2	3	4	5
2	2	4	6	8	10
3	3	6	9	12	15
4	4	8	12	16	20
5	5	10	15	20	25

The objects in this mathematical system are the natural numbers 1 through 5. The set is obviously not closed, since many other numbers appear as the result of the operation, multiplication. Test it to see if it has the commutative property. The easiest way is to draw the diagonal from × to 25. If the table is symmetric with respect to this diagonal—that is, if you folded it along the diagonal and the numbers on the two sides were exactly the same, 20 falling on top of 20, 4 on top of 4, etc.—then the system is commutative.

Does it have an identity element? Even if you didn't already know that 1 times any number leaves it unchanged, you could tell 1 was the identity element from the fact that its row is just a copy of the column headings, and a similar remark holds for its column.

Is there an inverse for every object in the set? No—there's nothing in the set to multiply 2 by and get the identity element. You can tell that in a minute by just looking down the column headed "2." "1" does not appear; therefore there is no inverse element for 2. Neither is there one for 3, 4, or 5 because there is no 1 in their columns, either. The test for the inverse property is simple in terms of the table. It is just the requirement that the identity element appear in every column.

To give more insight into the structure of a mathematical system look at the modulo systems.

Here is the multiplication table, modulo five, which was explained in Chapter Five:

×	0	1	2	3	4
0	0	0	0	0	0
1	0	1	2	3	4
2	0	2	4	1	3
3	0	3	1	4	2
4	0	4	3	2	1

If you analyze its structure the same way you did the one above, you see that it has the property of closure. Every object that appears is one of the numbers in the set {0,1, 2,3,4}. The diagonal test shows that it is a commutative system. Look for the row which is a copy of the column headings and you see that 1 is the identity element. This element appears in every column, except zero's; therefore every number except zero has a multiplicative inverse.

Custom and tradition dictate that the objects in a mathematical system be numbers, and that the operations be addition and multiplication, but they don't *have* to be. Let's take four letters as objects and * as an undefined operation.

From the table below you can deduce several facts about this unknown system.

*	*a*	*b*	*c*	*d*
a	*c*	*d*	*a*	*b*
b	*d*	*a*	*b*	*c*
c	*a*	*b*	*c*	*d*
d	*b*	*c*	*d*	*a*

It's handy to have a name to call an undefined operation—let's say "twiddle." Instead of saying, "Add *a* and *b*" or "Multiply *a* and *b*," say "Twiddle *a* and *b*." On the table above, the answer you get from twiddling *a* and *b* is *d*. Twiddle *d* and *c* and the answer is *d*. This gives you a clue that *c* might be the identity element. Look at *c*'s row and column and you see that it is, indeed, a copy of the column heading, therefore *c* is the identity element.

The table is symmetric with respect to the diagonal, so you know the operation of twiddling possesses the commutative property. Because *c*, the identity element, appears in every column, you also know that every element has an inverse. For instance, *d*'s inverse is *b*, since the answer to twiddling *d* and *b* is *c*. Finally, the only elements appearing on the table are *a*, *b*, *c*, and *d*, therefore the system is closed under twiddling.

The point to all this is that you were able to find out these things about the structure of this unknown mathematical system without knowing what *a*, *b*, *c*, *d*, and * are.

PROBLEMS

Answer each of the following questions for the tables given below:

1. Do the operations possess the commutative property?
2. Is the system closed under the operation?
3. Does the system have an identity element? If so, what is it?
4. Does each element have an inverse? If so, name each one.

TABLE A

+	0	1	2
0	0	1	2
1	1	2	0
2	2	0	1

TABLE B

+	2	4	6
2	4	6	8
4	6	8	10
6	8	10	12

TABLE C

×	1	3	5
1	1	3	5
3	3	9	15
5	5	15	25

TABLE D

*	*e*	*a*	*b*	*c*
e	*e*	*a*	*b*	*c*
a	*a*	*e*	*c*	*b*
b	*b*	*c*	*e*	*a*
c	*c*	*b*	*a*	*e*

7

Some Number Theory—Ancient Superstitions and Unsolved Problems

A good thing about the study of number theory is that it is concerned only with whole numbers. There are no decimals, no fractions, not even any negative numbers or zero, since the subject is based on the natural, or counting, numbers (1, 2, 3, etc.) which were used before any of these sophisticated adjuncts were invented.

Number theory goes back to very ancient times, and is rooted in numerology, just as astronomy began first as astrology. Though the Greeks called it "arithmetica," from their word "arithmos," meaning number, it is not the same branch of mathematics that we today know as arithmetic. *That* the Greeks called "logistica," meaning calculation, and they rather looked down their aristocratic noses at it.

What interested the Greeks was philosophy and the exercise of reason—let the slaves tend to the commerce, the trade, and all the necessary attendant computations. The surprising part is that their philosophy—especially that of the Pythagorean Society—was so imbued with beliefs about numbers.

Pythagoras, who had traveled in Egypt and Babylon absorbing both mathematics and mysticism, thought that numbers were the elements out of which everything else in the world is made, in much the same way that to other thinkers fire and water were the elements. He taught that number is the essence of reality and lies at the base of the real world.

About 530 B.C. his followers banded together at Croton, a Greek colony in southern Italy, into a sort of religious brotherhood devoted to the study of philosophy and mathematics, which to them were intertwined. They lived a rather ascetic life, seeking by rites and abstinences to purify the soul and free it from its fleshly prison, the body. Only men belonged, they took vows for life, and many practiced celibacy (though according to legend, Pythagoras himself married a young wife when he was past 60). Believing in reincarnation and the transmigration of souls, even into the body of an animal, they ate meat only on the occasion of a religious sacrifice.

The members of the order bound themselves with an oath not to reveal to outsiders the mathematical secrets they learned. Down through the centuries men have sworn by their gods and the stars, the bones of the saints and the beard of the prophet, but the Pythagoreans swore by a number. That number was ten—the holy tetractys.

Why did they pick ten? Because $1 + 2 + 3 + 4 = 10$. More clearly, the tetractys was represented by this triangular arrangement of ten dots, showing that ten is composed of 1, 2, 3 and 4.

```
   •
  • •
 • • •
• • • •
```

To them the first four numbers had a special meaning—they associated them with fire, water, air, and earth. Their sum therefore encompassed everything and stood for the ideal.

So persistent were they in this belief that they thought the whole universe must embody this principle. Their conviction that there *must* be ten heavenly bodies—although they could find only nine—led them to invent another one which they named the counterearth, explaining that it was always in the wrong part of the sky to be seen.

Their picture of the universe was of a central fire, or guiding force, around which revolved ten moving bodies. From the center outward, these were: the counterearth, the earth, moon, sun, the five planets known at the time (Mercury, Venus, Mars, Jupiter, Saturn), and lastly the stars, which they thought were all fixed to a single sphere and counted as one.

This conception was far advanced for the times and is much closer to the truth than the usual ancient (and medieval) idea of an earth which stood still, with all the other objects in the sky moving around it.

They identified the numbers with human characteristics, including a good bit of sex. The odd numbers were thought to be masculine, good, and celestial—the even numbers were feminine, evil, and earthly. There was a correspondence here with the Chinese, who also took the odd numbers to be bright, male, and beneficent and the even numbers to be dark, female, and evil. (You notice that the women got the worst of it in all this ancient symbolism. Does that prove that women then were more malevolent than men? Of course not—it just proves that it was the men who invented the symbols.)

In addition, individual numbers had their own distinguishing traits. *One* stood for reason, and was not considered a true number, but rather as the source from which all the numbers were generated, by adding ones together. It was not classified as either even or odd.

Two represented opinion—wavering, indecisive, as today we say, "I'm of two minds about the matter."

Four was identified with justice, because it was the first number that is the product of equals, i.e., two times two. We still use "square" with this meaning (or did, before bebop changed the connotation)—"a square deal," "fair and square," "a square shooter."

Five was the marriage number, made from the union of *two,* the first even (feminine) number, and *three,* the first odd (masculine) number, since *one* didn't count.

Seven was a virgin number, because, of the first ten, it alone is neither factor nor product—that is, none of the others is divisible* by seven, nor can seven be divided evenly by any of them, without a remainder.

Don't laugh at all this. Underneath the numerology, the fundamental idea in Pythagorean philosophy was that only through number and form can man grasp the nature of the universe. Sir William Cecil Dampier, in *A History of Science* (1949), said that "Moseley with his atomic numbers, Planck with his quantum theory, and Einstein with his claim that physical facts such as gravitation are exhibitions of local space-time properties, are reviving ideas that in older, cruder forms, appear in Pythagorean philosophy." Alfred North Whitehead in *Mathematics as an Element in the History of Thought,* said, " . . . we have in the end come back to a version of the doctrine of old Pythagoras, from whom mathematics, and mathematical physics, took their rise."

* Divisible means exactly divisible, with no remainder.

Figurate Numbers

Ask some of your friends what they picture in their mind's eye when you say "Three." Most of them will see this symbol:

$$3$$

A few (these people have trouble with math) see:

THREE

But the Greeks, because of their habit of representing numbers as configurations of dots, saw:

```
 .
. .
```

To them, numbers had geometrical shape. *Three* was a triangle. So was *six.*

```
  .
 . .
. . .
```

Ten, also, was a triangular number, as you saw on page 93. *Four* was square:

```
. .
. .
```

One square number could be transformed into the next

square number by adding an L-shaped border, called a gnomon (from a Greek word meaning "carpenter's rule").

There are always an odd number of dots in a gnomon. In fact, every odd number can be used as a gnomon to make a square number, as 5 is used to make 9 in the example above.

Any two consecutive triangular numbers (say 6 and 10) can be put together to form a square number like this:

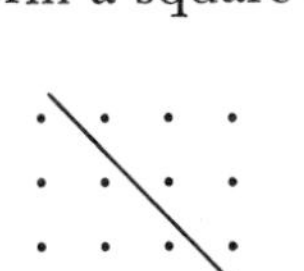

The total number of dots could be expressed as $6 + 10$ or as 4×4, using the number of dots on each side of the square. This is more compactly written as 4^2, commonly read "4 squared," a heritage from the Greek method of placing the dots in a square pattern.

The relationship above shows that $6 + 10 = 4^2$. Taking the next successive square number—25—yields $10 + 15 = 5^2$ and you can go on to discover a whole list of these. The computations involved provide many opportunities for practice in addition, subtraction, multiplication, and division, yet with the purpose of gaining an understanding of number relationships that are useful later in algebra and geometry—not drill just for drill's sake.

These patterns of dots show a relationship between number, the substance out of which arithmetic is made, and form, the substance of geometry. Figurate numbers lay the foundation for the study of series, a very useful branch of mathematics usually taught in high school as part of second-year algebra. Both the square numbers and the triangular numbers recur systematically but according to different laws. The discovery of these laws becomes easy if the numbers are represented by dots, but is not brought out at all in their representation by numerals. There is nothing in the appearance of 3, 6, and 10 to show you how to make each from its predecessor, but look at these dot patterns and you immediately have a clue:

```
  •          •           •
 • •        • •         • •
           • • •       • • •
                      • • • •
```

PROBLEMS

1. a. What odd number is used as the gnomon to form 16?
   b. To form 25?
2. Classify the following numbers as triangular or square:
   a. 15
   b. 16
   c. 21
   d. 25
   e. 49
   f. 28
   g. 100
3. What numbers from 2 to 10, inclusive, are neither triangular nor square?

Prime Numbers

A somewhat later and much more mathematically useful classification of numbers is into the categories of those that are prime and those that are not. "Number" here, as in all of number theory, means a whole number greater than zero— 1, 2, 3, . . . etc. Some texts call these *natural* numbers or *counting* numbers.

A *prime* number is a number (excluding one) which is exactly divisible only by itself and one. Why is one excluded? Partly because one is divisible by itself only. Another reason might be the historical feeling that one is not a number at all, but the source from which numbers are generated. A third, and stronger, reason you will see later in this chapter when the Fundamental Theorem of Arithmetic is discussed.

Applying the definition above, 5 is a prime number because the only numbers which divide into it exactly are 5 and 1. Six is not a prime number because it is divisible by 2 and by 3, as well as by 6 and 1.

These whole numbers which may be divided into 6 exactly, with no remainder, are called the factors of 6. Using this term, a newer and more economically worded definition of prime number is: whole numbers that have exactly two different factors are called prime numbers.

One way of finding prime numbers is by means of the Sieve of Eratosthenes, attributed to the Greek, Eratosthenes, who was the librarian of the wonderful ancient library at Alexandria and versed in many branches of learning.

To use this classical method, write down all the numerals from 1 through 100. (Fifty will be enough to give you the idea.) Since 1 is disqualified, cross it out. 2 fits the definition and is a prime number, so leave it, but cross out every second numeral after that. Three is also prime—leave it and mark out every subsequent third numeral. (You will find that some of them have already been crossed out.) Four is already gone, so go on to 5—a prime number—leave it and cross out every fifth numeral thereafter. Continue in this fashion to the end of the list.

~~1~~	2	3	~~4~~	5	~~6~~	7	~~8~~	~~9~~	~~10~~
11	~~12~~	13	~~14~~	~~15~~	~~16~~	17	~~18~~	19	~~20~~
~~21~~	~~22~~	23	~~24~~	~~25~~	~~26~~	~~27~~	~~28~~	29	~~30~~
31	~~32~~	~~33~~	~~34~~	~~35~~	~~36~~	37	~~38~~	~~39~~	~~40~~
41	~~42~~	43	~~44~~	~~45~~	~~46~~	47	~~48~~	~~49~~	~~50~~

The numbers that remain are prime numbers. Supposedly, Eratosthenes actually punched out holes in a parchment sheet, instead of just marking through the numerals, hence the name sieve. All the numbers that were not prime were sifted out.

Eratosthenes' Sieve went up through 100. Many college libraries contain a list, by D. N. Lehmer, of all the prime numbers up to 10 million.

The non-primes which sift through the Sieve of Eratosthenes are called *composite* numbers. Each of them can be expressed as the product of two or more other numbers—their factors. A good deal of time has always been devoted to this factoring process in mathematical courses, both arithmetic and algebra.

A widely used device to illustrate factoring is the factor tree—a sort of diagram. This scheme shows the factors of 6 like this:

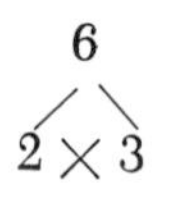

In case the first two factors are not prime, they, in turn, are factored and the process repeated until only prime numbers result. For example, 12 may be factored like this:

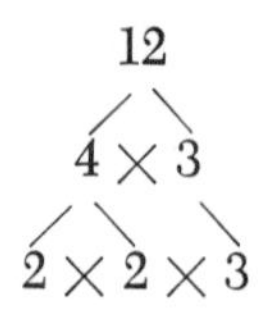

If you started with 6×2, which also equals 12, a different factor tree results:

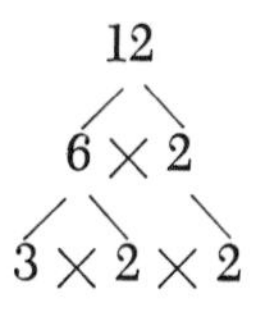

Notice that the bottom row of both trees is, except for the order of the factors, the same. In other words, no matter which way you factor 12, you end with the same set of prime factors.

Suppose you were factoring 20. Here are two possible factor trees:

Again the two bottom rows are the same, no matter how you start. This very important property is called the Fundamental Theorem of Arithmetic, which is: Every composite number can be expressed as a product of *only one* set of primes.

Here is that other reason for not calling 1 a prime number. If it were, then 20 could be expressed as the product of several different sets of primes, for instance: $5 \times 2 \times 2 \times 1$ or $5 \times 2 \times 2 \times 1 \times 1$, etc.

In computation, a common use of factoring is to find the least common multiple for several numbers, for example 8 and 12. A multiple of 8 means a number that has 8 as a factor. A common multiple would have both 8 and 12 as factors. You could, of course, just multiply them together, getting 96, but is this the smallest possible number that will fit the specification? No, it isn't. To find the least common multiple (abbreviated l.c.m.), first make the factor trees for 8 and 12:

The bottom rows show only 2's and a 3, therefore the common multiple will have to be composed of these numbers. How many of each to take? Use each the greatest number of times that it appears in any one tree's bottom row. You need $2 \times 2 \times 2 \times 3$, which equals 24, the least common multiple of 8 and 12.

Number theory is unusual in that it contains many problems that have resisted solution for centuries, although the problems themselves can be stated so simply that a child can understand them. One of these is the Goldbach Conjecture.

This is a guess that all even numbers greater than 2 can be expressed as the sum of two primes, for example, $12 = 5 + 7$ and $16 = 11 + 5$. In 1742 Christian Goldbach—mathematically an unknown except for this one thing—wrote a letter to Leonhard Euler, the great Swiss mathematician, saying that he had observed this to be true for every even number that he had tried and asking if Euler could prove it for *all* even numbers. Euler could not, and neither has anyone else been able to, although many mathematicians have worked on the problem since.

A mathematical statement cannot be *proved* merely by testing it for a large number of examples. Even if it worked in a million cases, the million-and-first one might not. On the other hand, a single counterexample—that is, a case where it is not true—will disprove the statement.

To prove a mathematical statement it is necessary to use general terms which will apply to *all* cases, following the rules of logic. A niche in the mathematical hall of fame awaits the person who can do this for the Goldbach Conjecture—or, for that matter, the person who can find a single counterexample to it, which hasn't been done either.

Another unsolved problem is that of the twin primes, a name given to any two prime numbers whose difference is 2, such as 5 and 7, 11 and 13, or 29 and 31. There are a lot of these pairs among the smaller numbers, but as the numbers get larger the twin primes become scarcer, suggesting that they may be about to peter out. The question is: Is there a last pair of twin primes or is the number unlimited? So far no one has found out.

Other unsolved problems are of a different type—that is, the answer to the general question is known and so is the method of obtaining a complete solution, but the computations required are so ponderous as to be impossible. For example: Is there a greatest prime number? Over 2000 years ago, Euclid, the great geometer, proved that there is not. In other words, no matter how large the size of a known prime number, there is always another one even bigger.

But when it comes to selecting a large number and testing it to see whether or not it is prime, that is a different matter. The most obvious way is just to divide it by all the prime numbers smaller than itself. If at least one of these smaller numbers divides into it without a remainder, then the number is not a prime. If none of the divisions come out evenly, then it is a prime. But the time required to work out all these divisions is astronomical. Even with computers, which can perform 1000 divisions a second, the elapsed time would still be huge in the case of these enormous numbers.

For centuries mathematicians have been devising short-cuts to this tedious process through formulas which make it possible to predict the outcome by dividing only by numbers in certain categories, instead of by *every* number. If the calculations had to be done by hand, this would still take too long to be feasible, but by combining the two methods—computers and formulas—startling results have been obtained. By using something called Proth's Theorem (a test for primeness) and a Standards Western Automatic Computer, which did the calculations in about 7 minutes, Raphael M. Robinson of the University of California discovered a large new prime number close to 600 digits long. This is the fourth biggest prime known at present. The largest one is $2^{3217} - 1$, which if written out in the ordinary fashion would contain 969 digits.

PROBLEMS

1. Classify the following numbers as prime or composite:
   a. 17
   b. 33
   c. 41
   d. 29
   e. 26
2. List all the prime numbers between 50 and 100.
3. Make a factor tree for each of the following:
   a. 28
   b. 63
   c. 45
   d. 120

4. Are there any twin primes in your answers to problem 2?
5. What is the least common multiple of 10, 12, and 15?

Perfect Numbers and Amicable Numbers

In their study of number relations, the Pythagoreans found a few numbers which they called *perfect*. Their criterion was that the number must equal the sum of its own divisors (not including itself). For example, 6 is divisible by 1, by 2, and by 3. Adding these, $1 + 2 + 3 = 6$.

As was their custom, the Pythagoreans attributed certain mystical virtues to the perfect numbers and spent a great deal of time searching for them. They are scarcer than you would think. The next one after 6 is 28, whose divisors—1, 2, 4, 7, and 14—do add up to 28. Numerologists from very ancient times have attached special significance to these two numbers. Six is the number of days in the story of creation, 28 is the moon's cycle around the earth.

The next perfect number after 28 is 496, then comes 8128, then 33,550,336. (Notice that the perfect numbers are getting farther and farther apart, and also that they all end in either 6 or 28.) Altogether the Greeks found a total of 5. Since then, others have been discovered, each being, in the mathematical world, something like the discovery of a minor planet to astronomers. They are becoming more and more huge—the twelfth one is: 2,658,455,991,569,831,744,654,692,-615,953,842,176. The seventeenth one, found in 1952, has 1937 digits. The enormous amount of calculation involved has gotten beyond human capabilities, the latter ones having been worked out with the help of digital computers. The search is still going on.

However, mathematicians' chief interest in them is not to discover another one, but rather to find the law underlying them. Euclid, whose famous Elements contained number theory as well as geometry, worked out a formula for finding perfect numbers that are even. No one has ever found an odd perfect number.

There is also a proof that all the even perfect numbers must end either in 6 or 28. (Maybe the ancients had something, in their beliefs about these two numbers.) But two main questions remain unsolved after more than 2000 years of mathematical effort. They are:

1. Is there a method by which all perfect numbers may be found?
2. Is there an odd perfect number?

If there is an odd perfect number, it must be larger than 14,000,000,000,000,000, as calculations have exhausted the possibilities up to there.

In their exploration of the relations between numbers, the Pythagoreans discovered certain number pairs that had a curious property—each was equal to the sum of the other's divisors. For example, 220 and 284 (the smallest pair):

Divisors of 220	Divisors of 284
1	1
2	2
4	4
5	71
10	142
11	220
20	
22	
44	
55	
110	
284	

The ancients called these *amicable* numbers and attributed to them the mystical power of attracting two people to each other. They were written on pellets and eaten as a sort of love potion, or, less drastically, worn as talismans.

The Greeks had a ready-made system of identifying a person's name—and therefore the person—with a number, because they used the letters of their alphabet as their numerals also. α was the symbol for both alpha, the first letter of the alphabet, and the number 1. β stood for beta, the second letter, as well as the number 2, and so on.

Maybe you wonder how they could count very high with an alphabet of fewer than thirty characters. They did this by grouping the letters. For example, ι, the symbol* for 10, placed in front of α meant 10 and 1, or 11. Thus ten letters took them through nineteen numbers.

The next letters, in order, stood for 20, 30, etc., and, in combination with the first nine, sufficed for any number up through 99. Larger numbers required three letters—for example, 112 was written by juxtaposing ρ, the symbol for 100, ι the symbol for 10, and β the symbol for 2.

The sum of the numbers represented by the letters was the number of the word. The Hebrews, too, used their alphabet in this same way and many Biblical passages are interpreted in this light.

So ingrained was the habit of associating numbers with the letters of the alphabet—and hence words—that the Romans continued the practice, although they had the Roman numerals, with which you are familiar, as number symbols for calculation. Just for fun, you might try working out the

* The older Greek alphabet had three more letters than the classical one, and these three were retained for counting purposes after they were no longer used for spelling words. Thus the position of certain letters is different here from the classical Greek alphabet which fraternities and sororities make their pledges memorize.

number of your name by applying this same system to our alphabet.

Getting back to amicable numbers, there is the story of a medieval prince, the letters of whose name happened to add up to 284. He looked for a bride with a name that would be equivalent to 220, believing that this would guarantee a happy marriage. Apparently he wasn't interested in either her looks or her personality—just the number.

Aside from these amorous connotations, mathematicians have searched for more pairs of amicable numbers for centuries. In 1747, Euler, the great Swiss mathematician, published a list of 60 pairs. About a hundred years ago an amateur mathematician found a remarkably small pair—1184 and 1210.

PROBLEMS

1. Show that each of the following does (or does not) fit the specifications for a perfect number:
   a. 46
   b. 128
   c. 496
2. Test the following pair to see if they are amicable numbers:
   24 and 36

The Fibonacci Sequence

A *sequence* is a set of numbers that can be written from a rule and they are an important topic in both algebra and calculus. Here is a famous one, the Fibonacci Sequence:

$$1, 1, 2, 3, 5, 8, 13, 21, 34, \ldots$$

Try to discover the rule for making this sequence. (Hint: look at any three successive numbers and see how the third one is related to the other two.) If you take the hint and examine 1, 1, 2, or 3, 5, 8, or 5, 8, 13 you will soon catch on to the fact that the third number is always the sum of the two preceding numbers.

This is called the Fibonacci Sequence after Leonardo of Pisa whose nickname was Fibonacci. In his great book *Liber Abaci,* published in 1202, which introduced algebra into medieval Italy, he wrote the following problem:

> "How many pairs of rabbits can be produced from a single pair in a year if it is supposed that every month each pair begets a new pair which from the second month on becomes productive?"

Worked out, this becomes:

First month – 1 pair	(litter of original parents)
Second month – 1 pair	(second litter of original parents)
Third month – 2 pair	(third litter of original parents plus first litter for bunnies born first month, who are now mature)
Fourth month – 3 pair	(fourth litter of original parents, plus second litter for bunnies born first month, plus first litter for bunnies born second month, who are now mature)
Fifth month – 5 pair	(fifth litter of original parents, plus third litter for first-month bunnies, plus second litter for second-month bunnies, plus two first litters, one for *each* of 2 pair born third month).

If you care to pursue this further you will get the first twelve numbers of the Fibonacci Sequence, which you see is already forming out of the number of pairs each month.

The Fibonacci Sequence is also exhibited in many examples of plant growth. For instance, the yellow center of a daisy is made up of two interlocking sets of spirals radiating in opposite directions. The number of spirals in the two sets is a pair of adjacent Fibonacci numbers—usually 13 one way and 21 the other, or 21 one way and 34 the other. Pinecone scales are arranged the same way, often with 5 one way and 8 the other, and so are the bumps on pineapples (8 and 13).

These same numbers crop up in art as well as in botany. In the classic sculpture of the Greeks a well-proportioned man 68 inches tall measured 42 inches from the ground to his navel and 26 inches from there to the top of his head. The ratio $\frac{26}{42}$ reduces to $\frac{13}{21}$ —two adjacent numbers in the Fibonacci Sequence. $\frac{42}{68}$ reduces to $\frac{21}{34}$ —also two adjacent Fibonacci numbers.

The quotient of any number (after the 1's) in the Fibonacci Sequence divided by the next number is approximately .6, and the farther you go out in the sequence the closer the quotient approaches .618. For example:

$$8\overline{)5.000} = .625 \qquad 13\overline{)8.000} = .615$$

No ordinary ratio, 618/1000 is what the Greeks called the Golden Ratio or the divine proportion. (They did not express the relationship decimally, but by a geometric construction which yielded two line segments in the exact golden ratio which we approximate by the decimal fraction .618.)

A rectangle whose width and length are in this ratio is

called a golden rectangle and was favored by the Greeks above all others. The Parthenon at Athens as originally constructed would fit into such a rectangle.

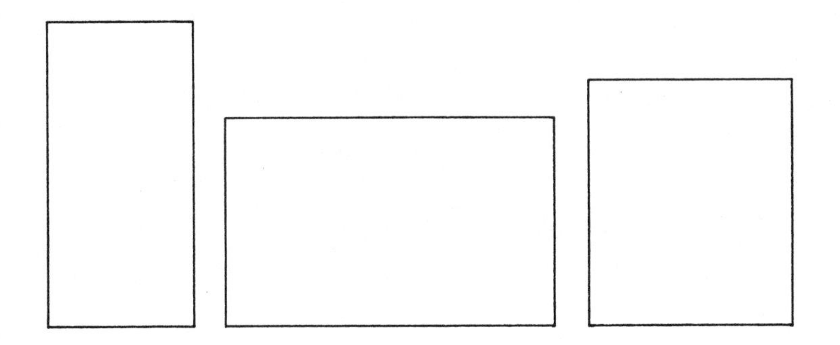

Of the three figures above, the middle one is a golden rectangle. In modern times, the psychologists Fechner and Wundt have conducted experiments which showed that many persons unconsciously tend to choose such a shape. For whatever reason, people who never heard of the golden ratio will pick it when given a choice of mirrors, book covers, or anything similarly rectangular. There is just something visually satisfying about that particular geometric form.

PROBLEMS

1. What are the next four numbers after 34 in the Fibonacci Sequence?
2. Divide each of your answers to problem 1 by its successor, carrying each division out to the nearest third decimal place.

PART III

8

Probability—The Science of Leaping in the Dark

Flip a nickel and who can tell whether it will come up heads or tails? Flip a truckload of nickels and, almost surely, they will come up close to half and half. In physics this principle is widely used to study the constant, violent, and *random* motion of molecules. No one can predict where any one molecule will go, and no one cares, but the action of millions of molecules can be foretold rather closely, like that of the nickels.

Small particles suspended in liquid or gas are kicked around by the molecules' movement. A photographic representation of the erratic, zigzag path of one of these particles looks very much like the drawing for a random walk problem in a mathematics text on probability.

In politics, the public opinion poll can make or break. Governor Rockefeller gave his ratings on these polls as his reason for not seeking the presidential nomination in 1960. Opinion research is a fast-growing science that talks in millions, and yet how many people do you know who have actually been polled? The researchers base their reports on interviews with a random sample, selected by probability mathematics.

Just taking a large number of people for the sample will not do the trick, as some have learned the hard way. The classic example is the old *Literary Digest* poll in the presidential election of 1936. The poll "elected" Landon but the voters elected Roosevelt, and by a landslide. How could they be so wrong? Ph.D. theses have been written on the *Digest's* errors, the consensus being that the sample was badly biased. The magazine picked their millions of names from telephone books, lists of automobile owners, and their own subscribers. In the depression year of '36, this was hardly a representative cross section of the population. As everybody knows, the *Literary Digest* folded after their fiasco. Today's pollsters use scientific sampling, with specialists in probability mathematics to reduce the margins of error.

Probability—defined as the study of phenomena in which chance plays a role—became a branch of mathematics in the seventeenth century when a dice player, the Chevalier de Méré, wrote to his friend asking what were the chances on throwing at least one 12 out of 24 tosses of a pair of dice. He made a good choice of friends, because it was Blaise Pascal, one of the foremost mathematicians in France, that he sent his question to. Pascal became interested in studying the problem, and corresponded with Fermat about it. Fermat, although his profession was the law, was a major figure in several fields of mathematics, and out of the work of these two men came much of the theory of probability. The subject that began with the study of gambling has since burgeoned to include problems in economics, sociology, heredity, politics, and physics.

Simple Probability

Mathematically, the probability of an event's happening is expressed as a fraction somewhere between 1 (a dead certainty) and 0 (no chance at all). The numerator of the fraction is the number of ways it *could* happen, the denominator is the total number of possible outcomes—both happening and failing to happen. If you flip a coin, the probability of heads is $\frac{1}{2}$—out of the two ways it can land, heads or tails, there is one possibility of its being a head.

If you draw a card from a full deck, the probability of getting a heart is $\frac{13}{52}$, because out of 52 cards there are 13 hearts. The probability of drawing a king—any king—is $\frac{4}{52}$. The probability of your card's being the king of hearts is $\frac{1}{52}$. There is only one king of hearts in the entire deck, therefore only one possible way in which that event could happen.

This is not the same as the odds. They express the ratio of the possibility of an event's happening to the possibility of its failing to happen. The odds on drawing a heart are 13 to 39. Out of the 52 cards, there are 13 chances of getting a heart and 39 chances of getting something else—a non-heart, in other words.

The probability of a non-heart is $\frac{39}{52}$. Add this to the probability of drawing a heart—$\frac{13}{52}$—and it comes out $\frac{52}{52}$, or 1. The total of all the probabilities of all the possible outcomes of a single trial of an experiment is always 1, and you can use that fact to check your problems. In this case there are just two possibilities—heart or non-heart—so the card is certain to be one or the other, and a probability of 1 expresses a certainty.

Probabilities are most easily understood in terms of sets. If set *A* consists of all the hearts in the deck, then the set of all non-hearts is the complement of *A* (see Chapter One). Together they make up the universal set. In Venn diagrams it looks like this, with the rectangle representing the entire deck of cards:

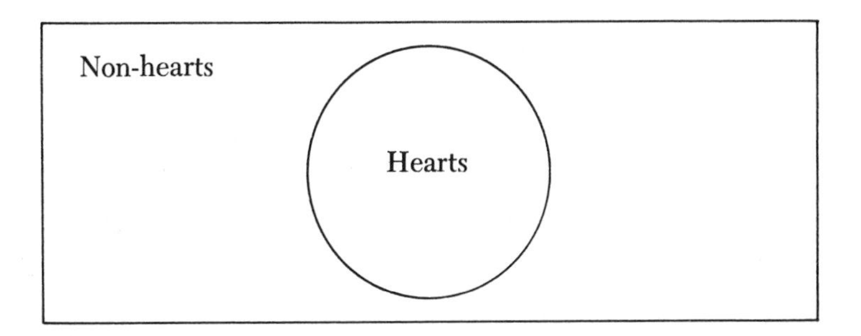

There are two widely held misconceptions about events that depend on luck. One is the theory of the maturation of the chances, usually called the law of averages. If you are flipping a coin and heads comes up a number of times in succession, many people say: "By the law of averages, the next toss is more likely to be tails." It is not. The probability of tails is exactly the same as it was in the first place—one-half. The fallacy comes in applying to the total of a series, part of which is already known, the formula of probability, which is designed only for the unknown future. If you are performing the experiment of tossing a coin (known to be perfect) twenty times and the first eight trials have already turned out to be heads, the best prediction of the outcome is that the remaining twelve tosses will most likely be half and half, giving a total of fourteen heads and six tails.

The other misconception is the opposite—a belief in streaks of luck. Some people think that, after a succession of heads, the next toss is *more* likely to be heads. They, also, are wrong. The probability of an event's occurring is still the same, regardless of what happened before—provided, of course, that the coin is perfect, the dice are true, and the deck is not stacked.

PROBLEMS

1. The days of the week are each written on a separate slip and put in a box. If you draw one without looking, what is the probability of getting Tuesday?
2. A bag contains a number of Christmas balls—all either red or green—and you take one out, blindfolded. If the probability of getting a red one is known to be $5/11$, what is the probability of a green one?
3. In your pocket you have 2 dimes, 1 quarter, 3 nickels, and a fifty-cent piece. If you reach in and take a coin at random, what is the probability it will be a dime?
4. If a single die is rolled, what is the probability that it stops with an even number showing on the top face?
5. A box contains a dozen pieces of fruit—seven apples and five pears. If you take one at random, what are the odds that it will be an apple? What is the probability it will be an apple?

Compound Probability

Suppose you are interested in the outcome of two chance events which are independent of each other. Say you roll two dice—what is the probability that one will come to rest showing a 5 on the top face and the other will also come up 5? It is easy to figure the probability of each even separately—out of the six numerals on a single die there is only one 5, so the probability of getting a 5 on one die is $1/6$. Since the conditions of the problem will be met only if there is a

5 on one die *and* a 5 on the other also, you might be tempted to add the two probabilities, but that will not work.

To analyze the situation, think of one red die and one white die and make a chart called the "sample space" of all the ways each number on the red die could be paired with each number on the white die. Always naming the red die first, you would have:

(1,1)	(1,2)	(1,3)	(1,4)	(1,5)	(1,6)
(2,1)	(2,2)	(2,3)	(2,4)	(2,5)	(2,6)
(3,1)	(3,2)	(3,3)	(3,4)	(3,5)	(3,6)
(4,1)	(4,2)	(4,3)	(4,4)	(4,5)	(4,6)
(5,1)	(5,2)	(5,3)	(5,4)	(5,5)	(5,6)
(6,1)	(6,2)	(6,3)	(6,4)	(6,5)	(6,6)

There are 36 ordered pairs in this sample space and only one of them (5,5) is the one we want. Therefore the probability of both dice coming up 5 is $1/36$.

You see that adding $1/6$ and $1/6$ will not make $1/36$, but multiplying them will. The rule is: To find the probability that a number of independent events will all occur simultaneously, multiply together the separate probabilities of each of them. For example, suppose you flip a coin, draw a card from a full deck, and roll a die. What is the probability that you see a head on the coin, a queen on the card, and a 3 on the die? The probability of a head is $1/2$, of a queen is $4/52$, and of a 3 on the die is $1/6$. $1/2 \times 4/52 \times 1/6 = 1/156$, much less than any one of them separately. Had you added you would have gotten a number larger than any of the individual probabilities, which is against common sense.

The National Aeronautics and Space Administration used this principle of multiplying probabilities in deciding which of three possible methods for making a manned moon expedition offered the best chance of success. They broke each of the choices—(A) Direct Approach, (B) Earth Orbit Rendezvous, (C) Lunar Orbit Rendezvous—down into major elements, from take-off to return. The probability of each element's success was determined, as far as possible, from previous performance. Then all these for method A were multiplied, giving the probability of successful completion of a moon shot by direct approach. B and C were computed in the same way, and from a comparison of the three, the lunar orbit rendezvous was selected as the most feasible. Here a decision of major importance was reached through the use of probability mathematics.

Often the problems call for the probability of one event *or* another. For example, suppose you win if one roll of a single die comes up 2 *or* 3. These are mutually exclusive events, since you can't get both a 2 and a 3 on one roll. In set language, the two sets are disjoint and a Venn diagram would look like this (see Chapter One):

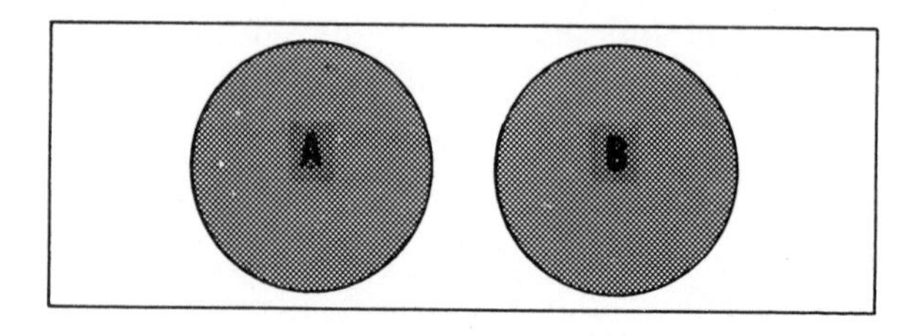

Clearly you have a better chance of winning on a proposition of this kind than on a bet specifying a single number. To find the probability you add the probability of getting a 2, which you already know is $1/6$, to the probability of getting a 3, also $1/6$, and you find the probability of winning is $2/6$. Incidentally, it is frequently better not to reduce these fractions to lowest terms, although it would not be wrong to say $1/3$. The probabilities are easier to compare and handle if left with a denominator which is the total number of possibilities in the sample space. In the case of a single die, this is six.

Not all problems of this type are mutually exclusive, however. Suppose you flip a quarter and then draw a card from a full deck. What is the probability that you see a face on the quarter *or* on the card? There is no reason why you can't do both. Bear in mind that in probability "or" usually means "and/or." The two sets are *not* disjoint and a Venn diagram will show them overlapping.

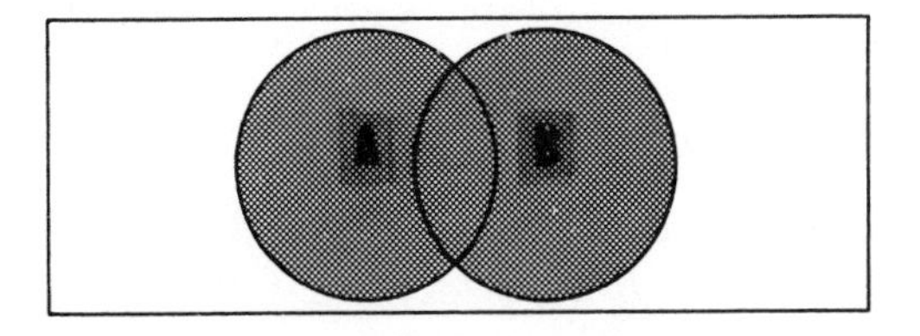

If you add the probability of seeing a face on the coin—$\frac{1}{2}$—to the probability of drawing a face card—$\frac{12}{52}$ (I am not including the aces)—you will get too high a number because you are counting the place where the two sets overlap twice. To keep from doing this, you have to subtract from the sum the probability of the joint occurrence. It is, of course, the probability associated with the intersection of the two sets which you found above by multiplying. Here it would be $\frac{1}{2} \times \frac{12}{52}$, which works out to be $\frac{6}{52}$.

The solution to the whole problem is: $\frac{1}{2} + \frac{12}{52} - \frac{6}{52} = \frac{32}{52}$.

PROBLEMS

1. A box contains four red balls, three blue balls, two yellow balls, and one white ball. If you draw one ball, blindfolded, what is the probability that it will be either red or yellow?

2. If you draw one ball from the box in Problem 1, replace it, and draw again, what is the probability that both balls will be red?
3. If Tom draws a card from a full deck, and simultaneously, Bill draws a card from another full deck, what is the probability that Tom or Bill draws a heart?
4. In one roll of a pair of dice, what is the probability both dice will come to rest showing threes on the top faces?
5. In one roll of a pair of dice, what is the probability the sum of the numbers thrown will be six?

Binomial Experiments

In a family of three children, what is the probability that two are boys and one is a girl? This is called a binomial experiment because the results fall into one of just two categories—boys or girls. If you call b the probability that a baby will be a boy and g the probability of a girl, then the problem can be set up as $(b + g)^3$. The exponent is 3 because we specified that this was a family of three children. Had we said four children, the problem would become $(b+g)^4$

To work the formula out, you have to brush up on the binomial theorem a little. Of course, you *could* just multiply $(b + g)$ by $(b + g)$ and then take that answer times $(b + g)$ again, but this is extremely long and tedious in problems involving families of eight or ten children. The binomial theorem provides a short cut, as follows.

In the expansion of $(b + g)^3$ the letters and their exponents are easily predictable. Leaving blanks for the coefficients, which we haven't worked out yet, $(b + g)^3 =$ $\_b^3 + \_b^2g + \_bg^2 + \_g^3$, as you can see by multiplying it out the long way, if you want to. The exponent of the first letter is 3, the power to which we are raising the binomial. Then in each succeeding term, that letter's exponent decreases by one. The second letter's exponents are similar, but in ascending order.

To fill in the blanks with the proper coefficients, follow Pascal's Triangle. This device, attributed to Blaise Pascal and probably used by him in De Méré's dice problem, is a sort of pyramid of numbers, following this pattern.

1					
1	1				
1	2	1			
1	3	3	1		
1	4	6	4	1	
1	5	10	10	5	1

Working from the top down, the triangle can be extended as far as needed, as you can see in any second-year algebra book.

Since each row begins with 1, that doesn't tell you anything. Look at the next number—hunt around until you find 3, the power to which we are raising the binomial. That row reads 1, 3, 3, 1—the numbers to fill in the blanks we left. Then you have:

$$(b + g)^3 = 1b^3 + 3b^2g + 3bg^2 + 1g^3$$

You are now ready to solve any problem about the number of boys and girls in a family of three. We are looking for two boys and one girl, so take the term that fits this specification—$3b^2g$—and fill in the respective probabilities. (These problems all go on the assumption that the chances are even that a child will be a boy or girl, which is not exactly correct biologically, since there are a few more boys born. However, use ½ as the probability in each case, which is mathematically near enough for the purpose.)

$$3b^2g = 3\,(1/2)^2\,(1/2) = 3\,(1/4)\,(1/2) = 3/8$$

There you are with the probability that, in a family of three children, there will be two boys and one girl. For other combinations, just use other terms of the expansion of the binomial $(b + g)^3$.

Three boys: $1b^3 = 1\,(1/2)^3 = 1/8$
One boy and two girls:
$3bg^2 = 3\,(1/2)\,(1/2)^2 = 3\,(1/2)\,(1/4) = 3/8$
Three girls: $1g^3 = 1\,(1/2)^3 = 1/8$

To check, add the four different probabilities. Since mathematically they cover all the possibilities of the situation, their sum should be one.

$$3/8 + 1/8 + 3/8 + 1/8 = 8/8 = 1$$

The Chevalier de Méré's problem is of this binomial type. Although there are many ways the dice could fall, for the purposes of his bet they were lumped into two categories—twelve (t) or non-twelve (n). Since he wagered on getting at least one 12 in 24 rolls of the dice, the binomial would have to be raised to the twenty-fourth power. It is no wonder he had to consult two of the most eminent mathematicians of his time—Pascal and Fermat. Furthermore, the probabilities of each term that contained a t would have to be calculated and then added together.

Fortunately, there is a much shorter way. Since the total probability of all the terms is always 1, find the probability that the Chevalier will lose his bet and then take the complement. He loses in only one case—no twelves—so subtract that probability from 1 and you have it.

Most "at least" problems are best done this way. Take this

example: The probability of a certain brand of thumbtacks' falling with the point up is $2/3$. If three such tacks are tossed simultaneously, what is the probability that at least one will fall point up? (By the way, a single thumbtack tossed three times or three tacks tossed simultaneously are exactly the same problem, provided the tacks are all alike.)

The probability of point up $(u) = 2/3$
The probability of point down $(d) = 1/3$
$(u + d)^3 = 1u^3 + 3u^2d + 3ud^2 + 1d^3$

The only term which does not contain a u is the last one.

Evaluating: $1d^3 = 1\,(1/3)^3 = 1/27$
The complement of this term is: $1 - 1/27 = 26/27$

Therefore the probability that at least one thumbtack will fall point up is $26/27$.

PROBLEMS

1. If three coins are tossed simultaneously, what is the probability two will be tails and one will be heads?
2. In a family of four children, what is the probability there will be two boys and two girls?
3. A warped coin has the probability of falling heads $5/8$ of the time. If it is tossed three times in succession, what is the probability it will be tails at least once?
4. In problem number 3, what is the probability that it will be heads at least once?

Random Number Tables

Public opinion pollsters are not the only ones to use random samples of the population. And population does not necessarily mean people, or even animate creatures. If you wish to sample hay, then the bales comprise the population. Most major industries in this country take random samples to check on the quality of the articles they produce. The technique of insuring randomness in the sample is most important; otherwise the conclusions drawn from it are out of kilter with the true state of affairs in the whole population. It usually requires the selection of numbers in some fashion.

You do not get random numbers simply by jotting down whatever pops into your head because, subconsciously, you will favor certain ones—maybe three or seven or whatever you consider your lucky number. There is some indication that if you say: "Pick a number from one to ten," most people will choose one toward the middle, avoiding the edges, like 1 or 10.

A random number has to be generated by some physical process which will assure that each number has an equal chance of being chosen. You *could* draw slips from a hat or deal cards, but after two or three hours of this, for some large-scale problem, you begin to wish for a shorter, easier method. Furthermore, fatigue leads to poor shuffling, with consequent loss of randomness, and slips are hard to mix properly. (There have been some scientific papers written on the question of whether the capsules used in the draft in World War II were thoroughly stirred in their bowl; or if, in fact, they were still somewhat layered, so that some numbers were more likely to be drawn than others.)

The answer is the random number table. It is quick, simple, and efficient. Besides, it looks considerably more businesslike to be sitting at your desk perusing a table than rolling dice, which could be open to misinterpretation.

In appearance a random number table resembles any

other mathematical table, but the numbers don't mean a thing. You look nothing up by row and column. Start anywhere and read in any direction—it makes no difference. Here is a short one I made by drawing cards numbered from 0 through 9 (the numbers are grouped merely for convenience in reading):

81961	91798	41508	72680
07898	93844	18687	37964
53739	75892	48228	58327
37729	04625	17534	20670

When you use a random number table you are actually using the physical process behind it. The table above provides you with numbers as authentically random as if drawn from cards, but spares you the exertion. They are much in demand. The Interstate Commerce Commission's Bureau of Transport Economics and Statistics puts out a *Table of 105,000 Random Decimal Digits.* The Rand Corporation, which goes in for this sort of thing in a big way, has a volume called *A Million Random Digits.* The reason it takes so many is because you use them up, like paper cups. After you have employed the first fifty, say, for some experiment, cross them off and don't take those any more. Otherwise, the same sequence of digits would occur over and over. Of course, if you want to be economical, you can go back and use them over, reading in a different direction—vertically this time, if you went horizontally before.

To give you a little practice in using a random number table, suppose you select five names at random from the telephone book, maybe for a television quiz, using approved scientific methods. (Why can't you just open the book and jab, blindfolded? Because the book will probably open at the pages you use most, therefore each name will not have an equal chance of being chosen.) In most cases, the book will have less than a thousand pages (not counting the yellow section), four columns to a page, and less than a hundred names to the column. Use the table above and, starting anywhere, take three digits in order. That gives you the page. Cross them off and use the next digit for the column number. If it is larger than your number of columns, skip it and go on until you reach a figure that fits. Mark these off, then take the next pair of digits to find the name, counting from the top of the column down. *There* is the lucky person. Do this five times, always using fresh digits, and you have a true random sample of five telephone subscribers in your community.

The random number table can also be a modern device to replace drawing straws. Suppose four college girls pool their money and buy a fur jacket, agreeing to take turns wearing it. Joan puts in 10% of the cost, Susan 20%, Jane 30%, and Melinda 40%. On the Saturday of the big game, naturally, they all want to wear it at once. They agree to draw, but the girls who paid more money think they should have a better chance. What to do? Borrow a random number table and assign each girl digits in proportion to her investment. Joan gets one digit, say 0; Susan gets 1,2; Jane gets 3,4,5; and Melinda 6,7,8,9. Open the random number table and read the first digit that is not marked out. Whichever girl has that number gets to wear the jacket—all fair, square, and scientific.

In case the situation doesn't jibe so neatly with the decimal system, the random number table will still work. Suppose three boys buy a boat—John pays ⅛ of the price, Steve pays 2/8, and Bill puts up ⅝. To decide who will get to use it on a given day, make an arrangement like this:

Number	*Winner*
9	John
8	Steve
7	Steve
6	Bill
5	Bill
4	Bill
3	Bill
2	Bill
0,1	(Skip and go on to the next digit.)

Each of the eight digits 2 through 9 are equally likely, and each has a probability of ⅛. John's, Steve's, and Bill's chances of winning are exactly the same as the fraction of the cost they paid.

9

Statistics—Meet Mr. Average

There is a connection between probability and statistics. In the theory of probability, we deduce the probable composition of a sample from what we know about the original population. In statistics, it is the other way around. We begin with the sample and attempt to infer from it the unknown composition of the population.

Statistics are essential to decisions made daily by doctors, manufacturers, chemists, advertisers, economists, weathermen—the list could go on and on. A step toward getting answers to many questions is to collect facts about them, and these are often number facts or *data*.

The science of statistics—the study of the collection and meaning of data—traces its beginnings to a small book written by John Graunt, a London haberdasher, in 1662. More or less as a hobby, Graunt compiled into tables the *Bills of Mortality*, which the city of London published every Thursday, giving the births and deaths for the previous week. From these tables (covering the years 1603 to 1661) he made several astute observations—the first attempt to derive from numerical data conclusions about social behavior and mass biological phenomena.

His little book makes rather grisly reading. It lists the number of deaths in each category, beginning with aged, ague, and running through the alphabet. As a medical record, the value of his tables is questionable, since the cause of death was determined not by a physician but by public officials called "searchers" who were, as Graunt says, "ancient matrons, sworn to their office."

From his tables Graunt noticed that the percentages of deaths from accidents, suicides, and various diseases remained remarkably constant. The same thing is apparent to us if we study, say, the figures for highway fatalities over a period of years. With all the millions of automobiles driven by people of widely differing ages, skill, and temperament, making hundreds of millions of trips over all kinds of roads and in all kinds of weather, it is surprising that the percentage killed varies so little from year to year. Although there is a large element of chance involved in the occurrences, there seems to be a certain regularity, or pattern, to them. The science of statistics aids in uncovering this pattern.

Averages

Broadly speaking, the subject of statistics is concerned with two things—the *average* and the *scatter*. Find the average man (or salary, or amount of rainfall, or whatever) and then describe in mathematical terms the way the others are dispersed above and below him. But which average? There's more than one kind, as you will notice if you stop and think about the way the word is commonly used. When you say "the average height of the men in this room," do you mean that someone added up all the heights and divided by the number of men? Or do you mean that if all the men were lined up in order, Mr. Average would be the middle one? Or, possibly, do you think of the average height as the one that occurs most often?

These three different kinds of average are all used in statistics. Collectively, they are called "measures of central tendency," but each has its own special name. The *mean*, or more fully, the *arithmetic mean*, is the answer you get when you perform the computations of adding the heights and dividing by the number of men. To take an example, suppose two of the men in the room are each 5.6 feet tall, one is 5.8, there is a 6-footer, and another—a former basketball player, naturally—towers 7.5 feet.

```
       7.5
       6.0
       5.8
       5.6
       5.6
5 ) 30.5 ( 6.1
```

The mean is 6.1 feet. Incidentally, this name has nothing to do with other, derogatory connotations of the word. If someone says "the mean temperature for July" this is not intended to imply that it is a bad old temperature. The reference is to the average temperature for July (though in some parts of the country it is certainly bad).

The *median*—a second kind of average—is the middle figure when the data are all arranged in order. In the example of the heights, the median is 5.8 feet. It tells you that there are as many men taller than 5.8 as there are shorter.

The third kind of average, called the *mode*, is the figure which occurs most often—in this example, 5.6. The name steers you right, since it is merely the most popular figure, regardless of where it falls in comparison to the other numbers.

Slight complications may arise in finding the median and the mode. Suppose the given numbers are 9, 8, 6, and 3. How to find the median when there is no single middle figure? In such a case you take the point halfway between the two middle figures—here it is 7, the midpoint between 8 and 6. Half the given numbers are above 7, half below.

In dealing with the mode, it may happen that several different figures occur the same number of times. For example, say the data are 15, 15, 16, 18, 19, 19, and 20. Both 15 and 19 are the modes and the problem is said to be bimodal—that is, it has two modes. There could also be data with 3 modes, or 4, or any number. However, there is always just one arithmetic mean and one median.

What's the use of having all these different kinds of averages? For one thing, the median often gives a truer picture of a situation than the mean does. Suppose a small company declares that the average yearly salary of its five employees is $6,000. And so it is—if by average they are referring to the arithmetic mean. But before you picture the five employees each getting something around $6,000 in his pay envelope, look at what a breakdown of the figures reveals: one worker is paid $3,600, another $4,200, one gets $4,700, one $5,500, and the manager makes $12,000.

Annual Salary		
$12,000		
	Mean	$6,000
5,500		
4,700	Median	$4,700
4,200		
3,600		

The reason the mean gives a distorted impression is because the figures are lopsided. The one high salary has a much greater effect on the mean than it does on the median. One very low figure would do the same thing.

There are times when the most useful kind of average is the mode. For instance, suppose the mean size of women's shoes sold in the United States last year was an 8. If the buyer for a shoe store—banking on this information—stocks mostly size 8's, he is going to have trouble fitting a lot of his customers. Neither would it do him much good to find out the median—that is, the size that half the women wear larger than, and half smaller. What he needs to know are the sizes that are sold most often—in other words, the modes.

From all this it is apparent that the unqualified word "average" has a very loose meaning and, whether by accident or by design, may be misleading. It behooves the consumer, or the job applicant, or the career chooser, to ask: What kind of average? Is it a mean, a median, or a mode?

PROBLEMS

At camp Billy keeps the following record of the number of lightning bugs he caught each summer evening for eleven days: 8, 3, 10, 5, 12, 9, 7, 3, 2, 3, 4.

1. What is the mean number of bugs he caught per day?
2. What is the median?
3. What is the mode?

The Scatter

An average alone—whether mean, median, or mode—can give only partial information about a set of data. For instance, if you read that a city had a mean annual temperature of 50°, does this indicate that the thermometer varied between the comfortable extremes of 70° and 30°, or did it go up to a sweltering 100° and down to a frigid 0° reading? Either way could average 50°. For that matter, so could the temperatures that astronaut Ed White's suit was subjected to during his walk in space—250° on the sunlit side and 150° below zero on the shady side.

Knowledge of the highest and lowest points enables you to find the range of the data by subtracting one from the other. In the first case above, the range is 40°, since $70° - 30° = 40°$. The word *range* is a technical term in statistics and is defined as the difference between the largest and smallest numbers in a set of data. It is a simple measure of the way the figures scatter, but has some shortcomings because it depends on only two numbers—the top and bottom—and tells nothing about the others in between. For example in the second case above, did the temperature shoot up to 100° only once during the year and the rest of the time go no higher than a delightful 80°, or were there many hot days in the 90's? Did it fall to zero during only one most unusual spell of weather or were very cold readings common?

A better measure of the scatter comes from computing the deviation from the mean of each individual figure, using positive numbers for figures above the mean and negative numbers for those below. Suppose a hypothetical city has these temperature readings during the year: (I'm sure you don't want to wade through 365 numbers, so, as an illustration, let's just take a typical day from each month.) 62°, 89°, 100°, 78°, 55°, 40°, 37°, 34°, 0°, 25°, 38°, 42°. Using the method explained in the section on averages, these temperatures have an arithmetic mean of 50°. Now, by subtracting, find the difference between each reading and the mean.

Temperature in Degrees Fahrenheit	Deviation from the Mean
62	+12
89	+39
100	+50
78	+28
55	+ 5
40	−10
37	−13
34	−16
0	−50
25	−25
38	−12
42	− 8

To distill information from these figures, the next step would appear to be to average the deviations by taking their sum and dividing by 12, the number of days represented. But try this, and you get zero as an answer. It always turns out this way, because the positive and negative deviations cancel each other.

It looks as if we are stymied, but there are two ways out. One is to disregard the signs of the deviations and just use the distances from the mean—never mind whether they are above or below. Now we have:

12
39
50
28
5
10
13
16
50
25
12
8

12) 268 (22.3

22.3, the average deviation, shows that, on the average, the temperature varied from the mean by that many degrees. A smaller answer would indicate that the data were clustered closer together—a larger answer, that they were more widely dispersed.

The other way out of the dilemma is harder, but it yields an answer, called the *standard deviation*, that turns out to be much more useful in the study of statistics than the average shown above. A typical problem might be to find the standard deviation for these scores: 11, 7, 8, 6, 5, 10, 9.

First we find the mean (8) and the deviation from the mean of each score, which turns out as follows: +3, −1, 0, −2, −3, +2, +1.

To keep from being plagued by the negatives, we square each deviation before we begin to average them. Squaring a number means to multiply it by itself, as -3×-3. Because of the rule of signs that minus × minus = plus, the answer is 9. Therefore after squaring, the deviation is no longer negative.

Deviation	Squared Deviation
3	9
−1	1
0	0
−2	4
−3	9
2	4
1	1
	7) 28 (4

Four is the average of the *squared* deviations. To get back into the original unit of measure, undo the squaring by taking the square root of 4, which is 2—the standard deviation asked for in the problem.

In tabulating a group of measurements, some are usually identical, of course. More than one man is 5 feet 10, or several students make the same score on a test. The bulk of these repetitions tend to come near the middle of the data. In fact, out of all the possible ways that figures can be scattered about the average, it is striking to notice that they very often fall into a certain pattern—so often that this pattern is called the *normal distribution.*

It shows up quite plainly if we make a dot frequency diagram like this, with one dot for each time a certain score appears in the data:

Failing Poor Fair Middling Good Excellent

You can see that the dots are stacked up near the center and thin out at the edges. Picture a series of lines connecting the tops of the columns and you have a rough approximation of the graph of a normal distribution. If we take thousands of cases, and allow gradations between the six categories (i.e., a score may rate better than poor, but not quite fair) so that the interstices between the columns are filled, the lines connecting their tops approach a smooth curve.

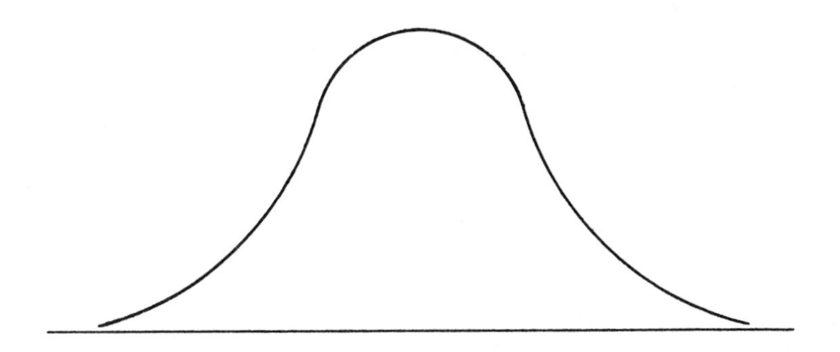

This famous bell-shaped *normal curve* fits the distribution of data connected with many human characteristics, such as the heights of adult males in the United States, or scores made on intelligence tests. It also jibes with some of the statistics collected in the study of plants and animals, as well as with events controlled entirely by chance. (Quételet, a nineteenth-century pioneer in the study of statistics, came up with the idea that, just as pennies pitched at a crack fall on one side or the other in a normal distribution pattern, so we humans are all aimed at one central mold but turn out to be near-misses because of the errors of chance.)

The usefulness of the standard deviation becomes plain here, because it is the yardstick commonly employed in showing the way data cluster about the average. As an example, let's look at the Scholastic Aptitude Test (SAT) of the College Entrance Examination Board, whose scores are expressed as numbers on a scale ranging from 200 to 800. The scale was calibrated by testing a large number of students and then using them as a fixed reference group.

The score of every student who takes the SAT, whether in December, 1962, January, 1968, or whenever, is reported on this same standardized scale.

The average (mean) of all the raw scores made by the reference group was pegged at the 500 point. As a handy method of showing how the other scores compared to this average, those one standard deviation above the mean were placed at the 600 point and those one standard deviation below the mean at the 400 point. Two standard deviations from the mean were at 700 and 300, respectively, as you see on the diagram below.

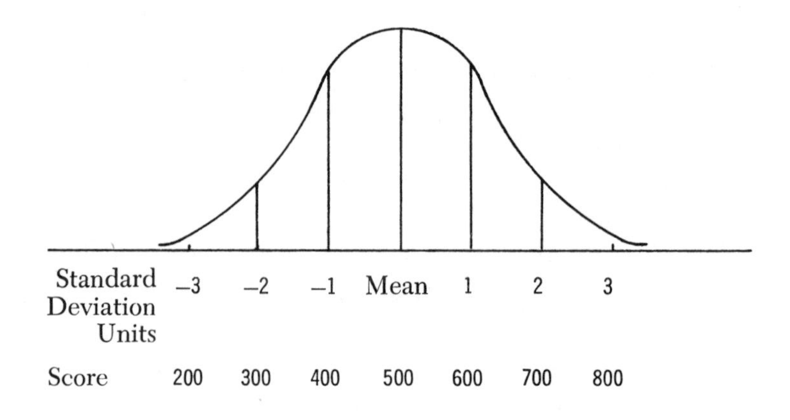

Why did they not go beyond 200 and 800 on their scale? Because statisticians have shown that if data are normally distributed 99.7% of all the items will fall within three standard deviations of the mean. They have also shown that 68.3% of them will come within one standard deviation of the mean. Thus, on this College Board scale, approximately 68% of the scores fall between 400 and 600.

PROBLEMS

1. Find the range for the following set of data:

   99, 112, 87, 91, 120, 98, 82, 112, 105, 118

2. Find the average deviation for these scores:

   19, 24, 16, 17, 20, 12

3. What is the standard deviation of the following data:

   15, 9, 11, 13, 5, 7, 17

Pictures of Data

After a mass of data has been digested and the information extracted from it, often the next step is to present the results in some sort of pictorial fashion that delivers the message at a glance. Every day in newspapers and magazines you see examples—circle graphs like pies with wedges cut out, bar graphs, straight-line graphs that go whooshing steeply upward to show a "whopping 10% increase." (This same 10% increase can be made to look very modest, with the line barely rising on the page, by simply using a different scale of vertical numbering on the graph.)

Then there are the pictographs, with rows of tiny stylized drawings of automobiles, one for each 100,000 cars that rolled off the assembly lines. The last one in the row is usually minus a wheel, or half the chassis, to show that the numbers didn't come out even.

There are two other kinds of graphs that are peculiar to the study of statistics. One is the *histogram*, which is something like a bar graph (see Chapter Two) but with no spaces between the bars. It is especially useful when a large collection of data has been lumped together into classes, without regard to small differences among them. For instance, you hear the weatherman say, "Temperatures around the state today were in the 80's."

Here is a histogram that shows the number of days in April with maximum readings in the specified categories:

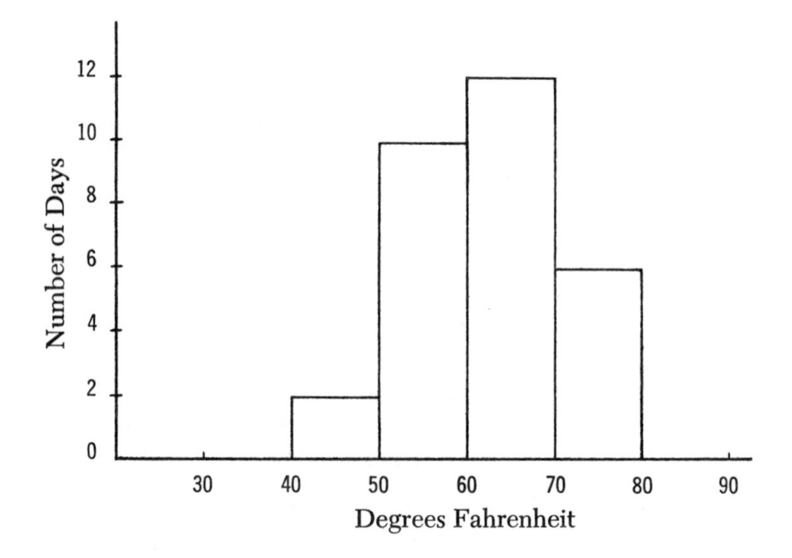

The numbers along the bottom show the boundaries of the classes. You see that there were twelve days with maximum temperatures in the 60's, but there is no way to pinpoint a particular reading as 62°, 67°, etc. Each individual number has lost its identity and become merely a member of the 60° class.

Of course you can't do mathematical calculations with

vague phrases like "somewhere in the 60's," so for computational purposes each of the twelve days is treated as if it had a temperature of 65°. (65 is chosen because that is the midpoint between the class boundaries of 60 and 70.)

As an alternate to a histogram, these temperature readings could be pictured by a *frequency polygon*. Here (using the method explained in the paragraph above) the data are handled as if there were two days with 45° readings, ten with 55°, twelve with 65°, and six with 75°. The points corresponding to the pairs (45°, 2), (55°, 10), (65°, 12), and (75°, 6) are located on a graph and straight lines drawn connecting them.

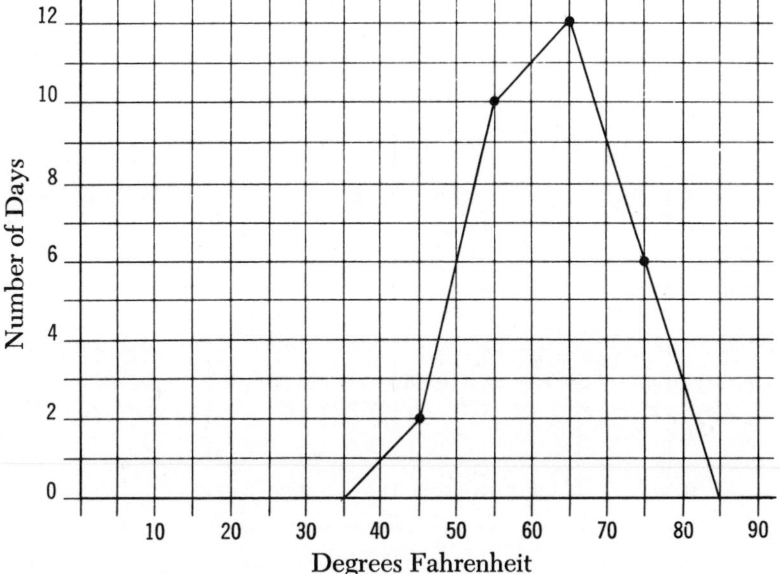

Notice that the lines are continued all the way down to the horizontal axis, forming a closed geometric figure, which the name "polygon" denotes. The line will touch the axis at 35° because that is the midpoint between the class boundaries of 30° and 40°—a perfectly legitimate class, even though there were zero days in it. The line touches the axis at 85° for the same reason.

PROBLEMS

1. This histogram depicts scores made on a test containing 50 questions:

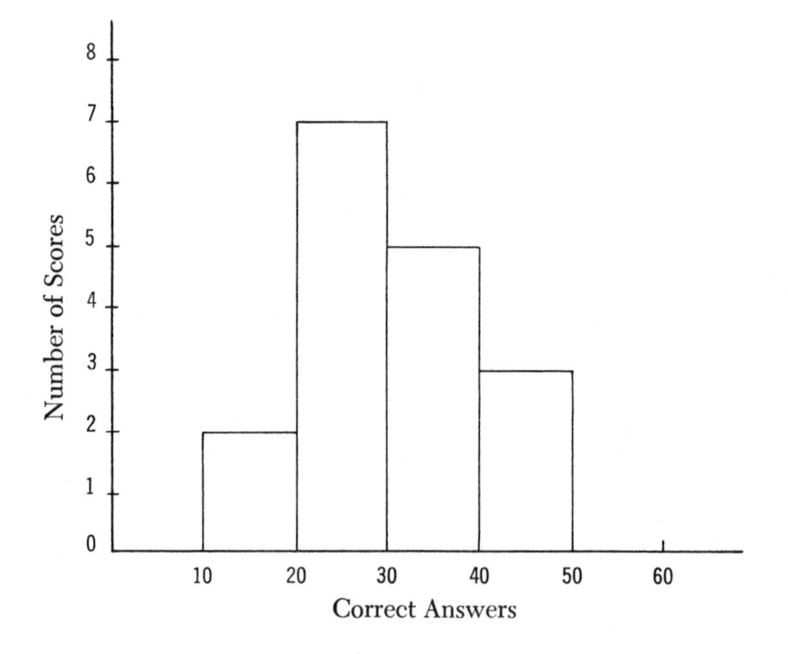

a. How many people scored in the 30's?
b. As shown on the histogram, what is the total number of people who took the test?
c. Can you tell if anyone answered all 50 questions correctly?
d. Did anyone miss all the questions?

2. Draw a frequency polygon of the data shown by the histogram in problem 1.

10

An Introduction to Game Theory—How to Outwit Your Opponent

If you want to negotiate with your parents about your allowance, maybe it would be helpful to know a little game theory, a branch of mathematics aimed at the study of strategy in conflict situations, which this is probably going to be.

Unlike some other topics in the new math, which—though new to the schools—actually are a hundred or more years old, game theory is genuinely new. The classic work on the subject, *Theory of Games and Economic Behavior,* by John von Neumann and Oskar Morgenstern was first published in 1944 by the Princeton University Press. Its beginnings are usually traced to the day in 1928 when Von Neumann read a paper to the Mathematical Society of Gottingen in which he outlined a rational strategy for matching pennies.

Do not confuse game theory—a study of games of strategy—with the subject of probability, which concerns games of luck. Strategy is controllable by the players, luck is not. True, most games contain some of both, but the proportion varies. Dice and roulette are almost entirely dependent on chance, but in bridge the play of the cards is extremely important, and both chess and checkers are wholly a matter of strategy.

Not that Von Neumann presented a system of bridge or of chess moves. The subject analyzes games as a whole, with the purpose of applying the same theory to gamelike problems in business, politics, and warfare, all of which are also characterized by a conflict of interest, the desire to win, and incomplete information about the opponent's plans. Games are but mathematical models of real-life situations. In fact, many games are themselves too complicated for complete mathematical study, since they would require billions of computations for an exhaustive analysis of all possible moves. Therefore simplified models are used.

Strategies

When you and your opponent are locked in combat what is the best strategy to follow? Whatever your scheme, there is always the possibility that your adversary will discover it and thwart you. If the two of you are anywhere near evenly matched, he probably will—it is naïve to suppose anything else. How, then, to prevent this from happening?

Game theory holds that there is only one sure way to keep your enemy from finding out your secret and that is: Don't know it yourself. In other words, randomize your strategy. Use some chance device, such as drawing slips of paper from a hat, but rig this device to conform to the odds which a study of the situation has shown to be advantageous. For example, in a game suppose you want to bluff 10% of the time. Write "Don't bluff" on nine slips of paper and "Bluff" on one. Put them in a hat, draw, and act accordingly. (This may not be very practical in an actual game, but it is the theory, not the practice, of the game that is being studied.)

No one—not even you—can know if you are apt to bluff in any particular case. Knowledge of your personality will do your opponents no good, since the decision is not made by you, but by fate. Even if they deduce that you are bluffing 10% of the time, they cannot tell which time it is.

Let's illustrate random strategy by the familiar game of Stone, Scissors, Paper. After the count of "one, two, three," two players each simultaneously show one hand—a clenched fist for stone, two open fingers for scissors, the hand spread flat for paper. If both show the same symbol, the game is tied. But if they show different symbols, the winner is determined according to the formula "Stone grinds scissors, scissors cut paper, paper covers stone."

Stone Scissors

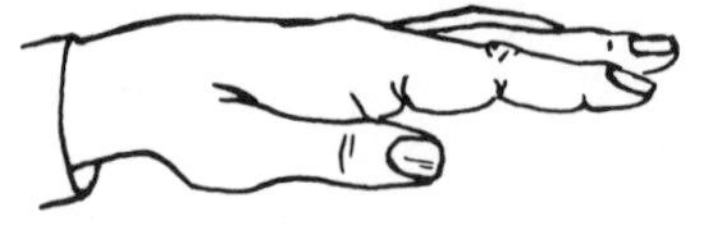

Paper

No one of these is highest—stone, for instance, wins over scissors, but loses to paper. Therefore, no particular way of playing is better than any other—all that matters is to guess your opponent's intentions and show the symbol which outranks his. In the same way, you are trying to keep your opponent from guessing your intentions—purely a matter of strategy. It is obvious that you should use each symbol one-third of the time, since all rank equally, but if you always show stone, scissors, paper in that order, he will catch on and beat you. What you need is an unpredictable pattern for mixing the plays.

To achieve this, you might make a circular card, divide it into three equal parts, and put a pointer on it. Spin the pointer (where the opponent can't see it) and play accordingly. He can't crack this strategy. In the long run you are assured of at least breaking even, no matter what he does, and you may win.

The outcome of the game is shown by a payoff table like this:

		Opponent		
		stone	scissors	paper
	stone	0	1	—1
You	scissors	—1	0	1
	paper	1	—1	0

The table is always read from the standpoint of the player named on the left in the horizontal position—you, in this case. You are the row player. The column player, named in the vertical position, is the opponent. A payoff of 1 means the row player wins 1 from the column player.—1 means he loses 1 to the column player. 0 means a tie. For instance, suppose you show stone and your opponent shows scissors. The middle box in the top row indicates that you win one point, because stone (you) grinds scissors (opponent).

Strategies are classified as *pure* or *mixed.* A pure strategy is an advance list of instructions telling you exactly what move to make in every possible circumstance, at every step of the game, according to what your opponent does. It is applicable to games like chess or ticktacktoe where complete information is available about the opponent's every possible move and there is no element of surprise. Similarly, the opponent could have all his possible moves worked out, taking into account every possible opening you might make. There then really wouldn't be the necessity for actually making any move. You could both just submit your complete lists to a referee and, after comparing them, he would be able to announce the outcome.

As you have probably already found out, if the two players of ticktacktoe are equally skilled, the game will always end in a tie. You only lose by making a mistake and you only win when your opponent makes a mistake. The fun consists in finding your way through the maze of possible moves, but as these are all laid out in advance, a machine could do it.

In chess the moves are so many and so complicated that the task of plotting all the possibilities is beyond even the largest computers at present. But in theory it is a game of pure strategy, and, once machines are developed that can handle all the computations, it will be possible always to predict the outcome between two perfect players.

Chess and ticktacktoe are called games of perfect information. Where this property is lacking, as in matching pennies or in Stone, Scissors, Paper, on-the-spot decisions have to be made. No advance list of instructions will do, since the game consists primarily of outguessing the opponent. Here a *mixed* strategy is called for. It is a fundamental principle of classic game theory, as set forth by Von Neumann, that the mixture should be determined by some random device controlled by the laws of chance. In matching pennies you can do this by merely flipping the coin, which will, in the long run, fall heads and tails each half the time but is unpredictable for any one flip. Spinning a pointer, as described above, does the same thing for the game of Stone, Scissors, Paper.

PROBLEMS

1. Make a payoff table for a game of matching pennies between two players.
2. Suppose, in a game of Stone, Scissors, Paper, the points are not evenly divided, but a win with stone is worth 5 points, with scissors 3 points, and paper 1 point. Make the payoff table for such a game.

Saddle Points

To begin with, let's take a hypothetical game with the following payoff table:

		Opponent	
		Strategy *X*	Strategy *Y*
You	Strategy *A*	1	5
	Strategy *B*	3	4

As always, the table is read from the standpoint of the horizontal row player—you. The numbers represent your gains. This type of game is called a two-person zero-sum game—that is, what one player gains the other loses. Therefore these numbers also represent losses for your opponent, the vertical column player.

In deciding between the two courses open to you (the two rows), you would like to choose Strategy *A*, which offers a chance of gaining 5 points. However, you must take into consideration the possibility that your opponent will anticipate this and counter with his Strategy *X*, thus limiting you to a gain of only 1 point. The sounder choice is your Strategy *B*, in which you are assured of a gain of at least 3 points, no matter what he does, and you may get 4. In making your decision, it behooves you to look at the *lowest* number in each row, which represents a more realistic view of the outcome.

Similarly, since these entries in the table stand for your opponent's losses, he should take warning from the *highest* number in each vertical column, since it is likely that you will push his losses as high as possible in the column which he chooses. His best move is Strategy *X*, in which he cannot possibly lose more than 3 points.

When these two points coincide, as they do in this example—3 is at once the lowest number in its row and the highest in its column—3 is called a *saddle point.* "Saddle" is used here in its geographical meaning—a low point in the crest line of a ridge. Think of yourself as following a path along the crest of a mountain. It goes up and down, but dips to its lowest point at a mountain pass. Meanwhile your opponent is driving up a road perpendicular to your path. His road goes up and up until it reaches the pass and then descends on the other side of the mountain. The two courses intersect at the pass, which is simultaneously the lowest point for you and the highest point for him. In the same way, 3 is a saddle point on the table given on page 149.

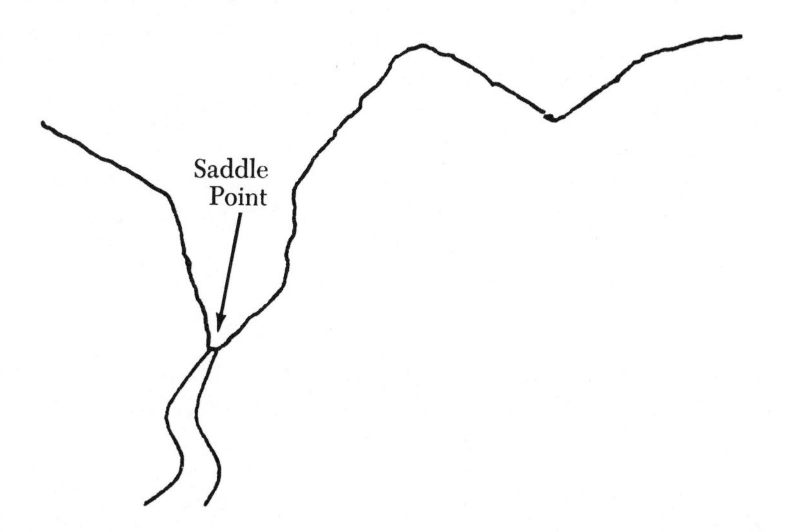

This is obviously a lopsided game, since you, the row player, gain in every case. A more competitive game would have some negative numbers in the table, meaning that there were courses of action open in which you might lose to your opponent, the column player. For example:

		Opponent	
		Strategy *X*	Strategy *Y*
You	Strategy *A*	—1	6
	Strategy *B*	2	3

The saddle point is 2, which is the lowest (minimum) in its row and the highest (maximum) in its column. By accepting in advance the possibility that information about your strategy may leak out and planning accordingly, you are protected against the calamitous effect of such a leak. In the same way your opponent protects himself against the possibility that you may spy out his plans. The solution of the game is predictable; the outcome (that you will win 2 points) is known and the game is said to be *strictly determined,* or stable. This is always true if a saddle point exists.

But suppose there is no saddle point? Take this example:

		Opponent	
		Strategy *X*	Strategy *Y*
You	Strategy *A*	0	1
	Strategy *B*	2	—1

Zero, the lowest number in the first horizontal row, is not the highest in its vertical column. Neither is —1, the lowest number in the second horizontal row, the highest in *its* column. The outcome is not strictly determined. If you pick Strategy *B,* seeking to gain 2 points, your opponent may choose his Strategy *Y* and inflict a 1-point loss on you instead. However, if you have found out that he *is* going to use Strategy *Y*, you would change to your Strategy *A* and gain 1 point. But if he knows this, he will also change to Strategy *X* and break even (0 represents a tie). So it goes, back and forth—the game is not stable.

What is the best way to play such a game? Clearly your only hope of winning is by preventing your opponent from finding out your plans in advance. If you play this game over and over, you should mix your strategies, sometimes using *A*, and sometimes *B*. To keep the pattern of your mixture unguessable, it should be determined by some random device, just as in the game of Stone, Scissors, Paper discussed at the beginning of this chapter.

The theorem at the heart of Von Neumann's game theory is that any game of this type can always be turned into a strictly determined game by using a mixed strategy, if the pure strategies are mixed in accordance with the proportions given by the laws of chance. (More advanced treatments of the subject give formulas for figuring out the proportions used in the mixture.) Every game of this type has a solution.

PROBLEMS

In the following payoff tables, which are strictly determined? What are the saddle points in each of these cases?

1. Opponent

You	7	5
	6	4

2. Opponent

You	1	0
	0	2

3.

Opponent

You	3	1
	4	0

4.

Opponent

You	6	3
	4	5

PART IV

11

Non-Metric Geometry—So You Think a Circle Has To Be Round?

The modern point of view is not geometry, but geometries, including some strange ones. For instance, there is projective geometry in which the figures are pictured as if drawn on a slide and thrown on a flat screen from various angles. The idea is to find what properties remain unchanged throughout these distortions. In topology—a geometry of form without size or shape—we go much, much farther. Some of the figures, as if made of rubber, are continuously deformed by stretching, squeezing, and twisting until any semblance of their original appearance is lost. A circle, deprived of its roundness, might look like this:

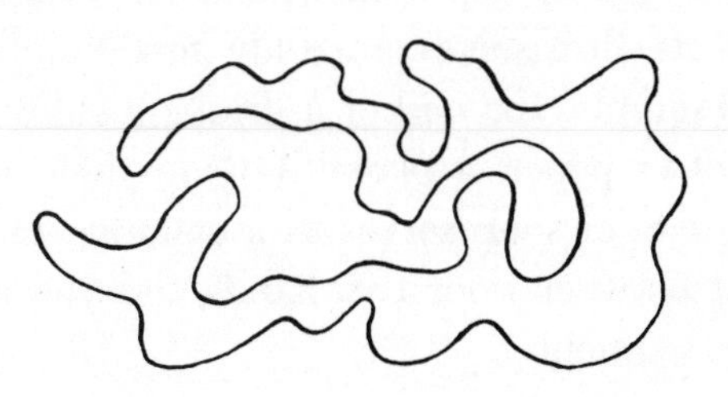

About the only property that's left is that it has an inside and an outside, although it's a little hard to tell which is which.

The traditional account of the origin of geometry is that the Egyptians were obliged to invent it because of practical matters involving real estate taxes. Herodotus, the historian, says that the king divided the land among the Egyptians, giving each one an equal-sized piece, and levied taxes accordingly. Each year, at the flooding of the Nile, some of the land was torn away. When the owners notified the king, he sent surveyors to measure what was left and adjusted the taxes proportionally.

By Plato's time, the character of geometry had changed. In the *Republic,* after pointing out that it was ludicrous to call the subject land-measuring, he writes of geometers:

> I think you know that although they use visible figures and argue about them, they are not thinking about these figures but of those things which the figures represent; thus it is the square in itself and the diameter in itself which are the matter of their arguments, not that which they draw; similarly, when they model or draw objects . . . they use them in turn as images, endeavoring to see those absolute objects which cannot be seen otherwise than by thought.

It is important to remember this viewpoint in studying geometry. Points and lines are ideas—the marks you make on your paper merely represent them. Drawings and even physical objects themselves are only models of geometric figures. For example, the end of a drinking straw suggests a circle; a sheet of paper, a plane. A tennis ball represents a sphere and a can of soup serves as a cylinder. Hold a piece of string taut between your two hands and you are demonstrating a line segment.

Bear in mind that a line has *no* endpoints, but may extend indefinitely in each direction; a line *segment* has *two* endpoints, and a ray has *one* endpoint (the side of an angle is an example of a ray). A line segment can be measured, but a line cannot, since it has no beginning or end. Neither can a ray, since it has no end, only a beginning. A ray without its endpoint is a half line.

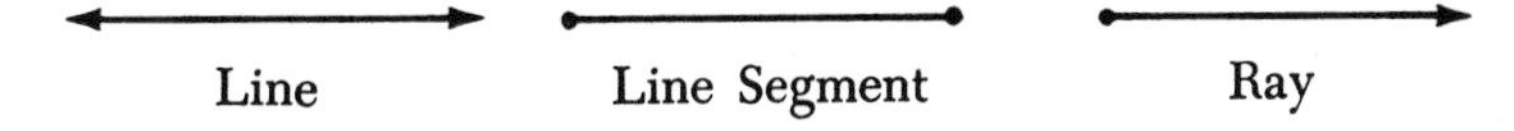

Line Line Segment Ray

These may (or may not) be marked with arrows. Just remember that if there is no point there to stop it, the line keeps on going, although only part of it can be shown on the paper.

Topology

If you see in your textbooks mention of the Jordan curve and the four-color map problem, this does not refer to the Middle Eastern political situation, as you might suppose. They are talking about topology, a new branch of mathematics whose growth has been phenomenal. Monsieur Jordan, a French mathematician, stated the following fundamental theorem of the subject: A simple closed curve in the plane divides the plane into exactly two regions, one inside the curve and one outside. Even if the plane is a sheet of rubber that is drastically deformed by stretching, shrinking, or twisting (everything is fair except tearing), this property persists. A simple closed curve remains a simple closed curve under all topological transformations.

The phrase "simple closed curve" is rather misleading.

"Closed" is straightforward enough—that just means it ends at the same point it started from. But "simple," used in this mathematical sense, means that it does not intersect itself. The diagram at the beginning of this chapter is a simple closed curve, but the following is not:

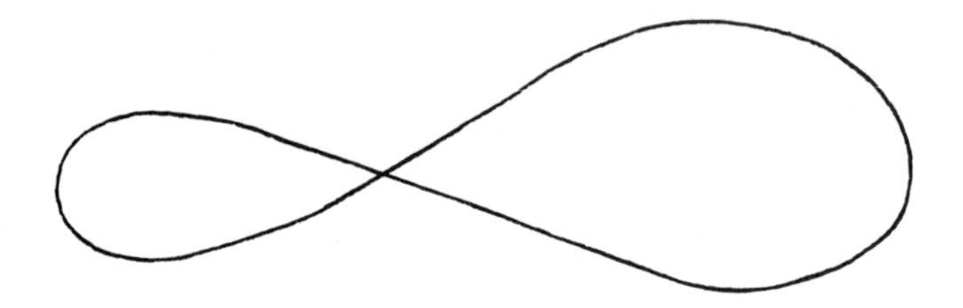

Neither does "curve" mean that the line can't be straight. Triangles, squares—in fact, all the polygons—are simple closed curves. Since the figures are distorted at will, straightness or curvature are only temporary properties of the line segment and have nothing to do with the underlying truth of the theorems.

Extending this idea to three dimensions, a simple closed surface is a space figure which does not intersect itself and which divides the space in which it lies into an interior and an exterior. Think of a single soap bubble—its iridescent film is a model of a simple closed surface.

As to the four-color map problem, it is this: Suppose you are making a map, either flat or on a globe, and, as is customary, you want to use different colors for adjoining countries, so the boundaries will show up. What is the least number of colors you can get by with? Since the size and shape of the countries have nothing to do with the problem and only the position matters, it properly belongs in topology, another name for which is *analysis situs*—Latin for the study of position.

No map has ever been found that requires more than four colors, but neither have the topologists arrived at a proof for this fact. They *have* been able to prove that five will always suffice, however. Since there is neither a proof for a four-color theorem nor a counterexample disproving it, the matter is hanging fire at present. Try to find one or the other, if you want to.

Although topology is a creation of the last hundred years, there were a few isolated earlier discoveries, notably by the Swiss mathematician Leonhard Euler. His solution of the Seven Bridges of Königsberg problem, made when he was court mathematician to Frederick the Great, is one of the foundation stones of topology.

This problem—a famous one in his day—is about the seven bridges connecting an island at the forks of the river Pregel, the two river banks, and the land between the forks, located as you see in this diagram.

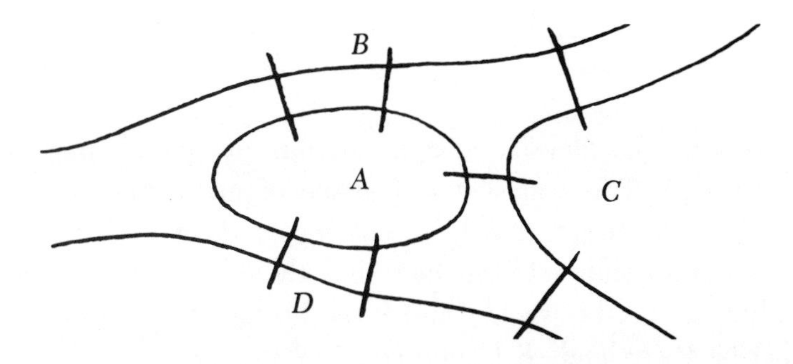

The townspeople of Königsberg (now Kaliningrad, since the Russians took over that part of Germany after World War II) amused themselves by trying to take a walk in such a way that they crossed each bridge once and only once. Some said it was impossible, some were doubtful, but Euler found no one who had actually done it.

Theoretically you could solve it by listing all possible routes over the seven bridges and seeing if any fit the conditions, but that would be extremely long and tedious, because there are a very large number of possible combinations. Euler looked for a way of analyzing the problem first to see whether a solution was possible. He did this by replacing the four land areas by points *A*, *B*, *C*, *D* and the bridges by lines connecting them. Although there is no such drawing in his memoir on the subject, you *could* make a diagram something like this to represent the situation:

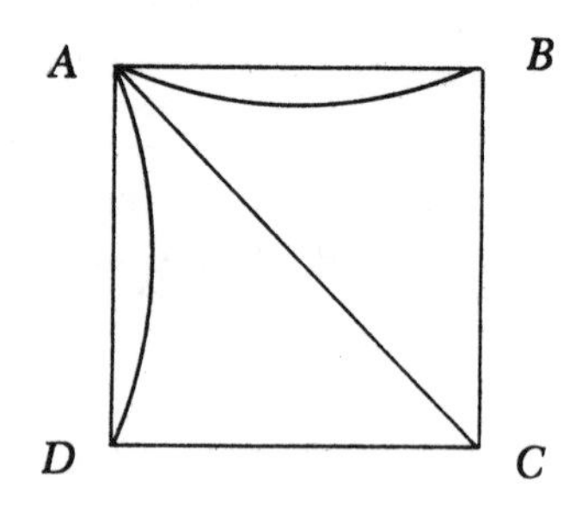

Of course, this doesn't look at all like an actual map of Königsberg. The real size and shape of either the island, the river, or the bridges have nothing to do with it. What the diagram shows is the fact that there are five bridges leading to *A* (the island) and three bridges to each of the other pieces of land—*B*, *C*, and *D*.

The problem then reduces to the question of whether you can trace this diagram in one swoop, without lifting your pencil from the paper or recrossing your path. If you can, the puzzle is solvable; if you can't, it is impossible. Euler found the underlying mathematical principle. If every vertex has an even number of lines converging there, the problem can be solved. It can also be solved if there are two vertices where an odd number of lines meet, but if there are more than two such odd vertices, the problem is impossible. (There is no figure with exactly one odd vertex; in fact, there is no figure with an odd number of odd vertices.)

In the Königsberg case, all four vertices have an odd number of lines (bridges), therefore there is no solution and the people of Königsberg are wasting their time trying to take such a walk.

Euler's most important contribution to topology was not the solution of this puzzle, but his famous formula about the relationship between the number of vertices, edges, and faces of a polyhedron, which later became one of the central theorems of the subject. Take, as an example of a polyhedron, the room where you're sitting. The faces are the planes —the walls, ceiling, and floor. The edges are the lines where they meet—the corners of the room and the places around the ceiling and floor where the builders put moldings. The vertices are the points where the edges meet.

Euler's formula is:

$$V - E + F = 2$$

Count them for your own room and (if it is the usual shape) you will get: 8 vertices, 6 faces, and 12 edges. Substituting in the formula, $8 - 12 + 6$ does equal 2. It will if your room is octagonal or any other polyhedral shape, or even if you are in the Fun House with slanting floor and crazy walls. These are all simple polyhedrons—simple because there is no hole through them. In topology, a hole means something like the hole in a doughnut, which would correspond to a tunnel through your room. It does not mean a hole such as might be knocked in the wall.

Since this theorem does not depend on the areas of the

faces or the lengths of the edges, but only concerns their number, it obviously has a topological nature. Descartes observed the relationship a hundred years before Euler did, but Euler proved it for all simple polyhedrons and it carries his name.

Topology as a separate study got under way about the middle of the nineteenth century with the discoveries of Moebius, a German geometer, and others. The Moebius strip is a surface with only one side. Most surfaces have two—for instance, this page, which is printed on both its sides. A bug, if he were prevented from crossing over the edges, could never crawl from one side to the other.

To make a Moebius strip, unroll a length of paper—it will show up better if the two sides are different colors—give it a half twist, and scotch tape the ends together so that you have a smooth continuous band, but with a twist in it.

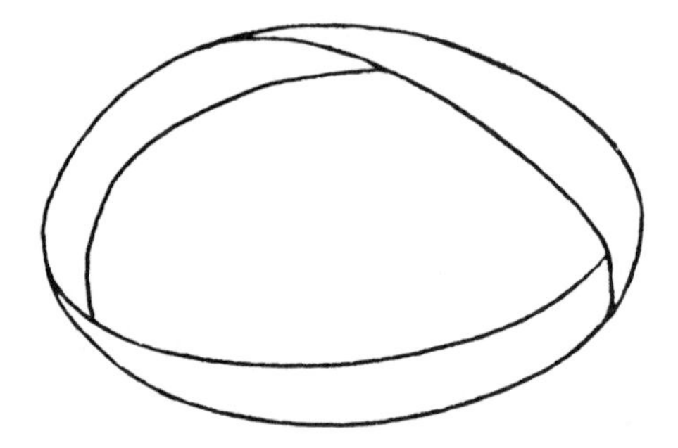

A bug crawling along the middle of the blue side will soon be on the white side without ever crossing the edge. Furthermore, there is only one edge. Trace it with your finger and you see that it is a single closed curve. If you had pasted the paper together without giving it a twist so that you had an ordinary band, its edges would be two separate curves.

Try what will happen if you cut the strip along a center line parallel to the edge. Most everybody will say that you will get two strips, but you don't. It makes a new strip, twice as long and half as wide. Now make another cut the same way as before on this second strip. This time you do get two separate strips, but intertwined.

PROBLEMS

1. Which of the following are simple closed curves?

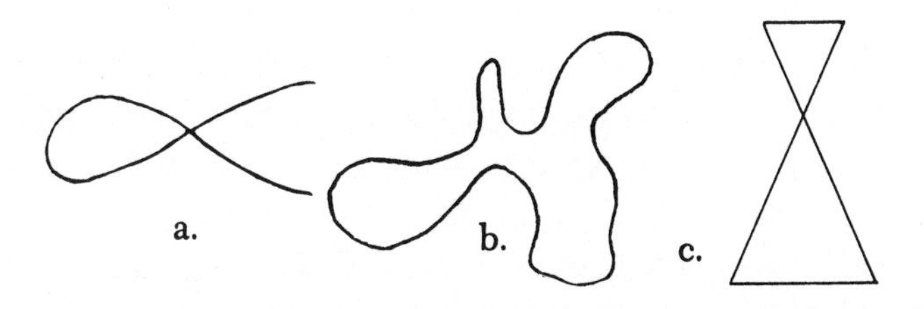

2. Which of the following can be traced without lifting the pencil from the paper or recrossing the line it makes?

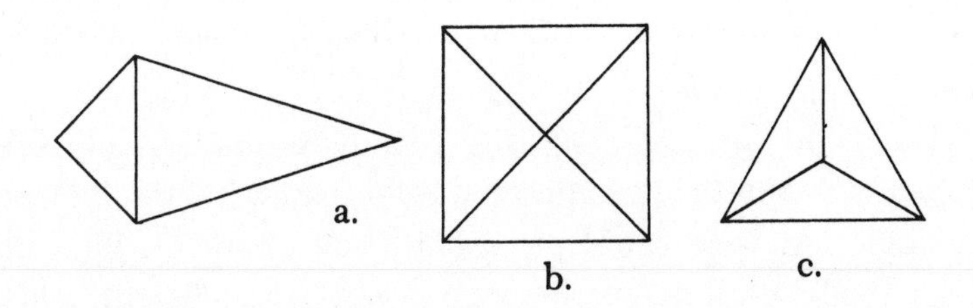

3. How many faces does a polyhedron have, if it has 12 vertices and 30 edges?

Other Non-Metric Geometry

Topology is a non-metric geometry, because it has nothing to do with size, but there are also other kinds. The criterion is whether the ideas of distance and measurement are introduced. In non-metric geometry, no line is said to be three inches long, no angle is specified as 45 degrees. The only numbers used are for counting sides, vertices, faces, etc.—not measuring them.

Non-metric geometry concerns space perception, either two- or three-dimensional. Nowadays, the concept of space is introduced as a set of points. Think of a swarm of immobilized flies filling your room. True, a fly is too fat to represent a point very well (since a point has no dimensions at all—only position), but so is the conventional pencil mark you make to represent a point on the plane of your paper. Picture an oversize sheet of cellophâne stretched across the room—it divides it into two half spaces, the set of points on one side of the cellophane plane and the set of points on the other. The plane is not in either half space.

Out of the set of points in space, various subsets can be formed according to the conditions laid down in each case. The simplest subset in each category is called a simplex. The simplest of the simplexes is a set consisting of just one point. Since this single point has no length, width, or thickness, it is a 0-simplex.

A straight line segment is a 1-simplex, having only one dimension—length. If some of the flies drew themselves up in single file, they could represent a line segment, but you don't really need all of them. Any two are sufficient, since through any two different points in space there is exactly one straight line. In other words, a set of two points will determine a straight line.

A set of three points in space, if they are not all in the same straight line, will determine a triangle. With its interior, a triangle is the simplest plane figure—a 2-simplex, with two dimensions, length and width.

A set of four points in space, if they are not all in the same plane, determines a tetrahedron (a pyramid on a triangular base). A tetrahedron has four faces, each of which is a triangle. It is a three-dimensional figure, like all of us, with length, width, and height. From the non-metric point of view, it is the simplest and is called a 3-simplex.

These four simplexes—point, line segment, triangular region, and solid tetrahedron—are the building blocks out of which other figures are made. Any polyhedron is the union of a finite number of simplexes, whether it takes one or a million.

Another geometry of the non-metric kind is projective geometry. You can see that it is non-metric if you hold a pencil over a table with a light above it. The shadow, which is a sort of projection of the shape of the pencil, changes in length as you vary the angle at which you are holding the pencil. Stand it upright and the shadow is very short; hold it horizontally and the shadow is always larger than the size of the pencil. The measure of the length of the pencil, a metric property, is not preserved in its projected image, the shadow.

Projective geometry originated during the Renaissance with the invention of perspective drawing. In ancient times the relative size of figures in a painting was dictated by the subjects' social position. The king was always the largest, then the next most important person, and so on down to the —literally—little people.

During the fourteenth century, painters began to try for a realistic representation of a three-dimensional scene on their two-dimensional canvas, which they thought of as a transparent window looking onto the visible world beyond. In this concept, rays of light come from every point in the scene, intersect the canvas, and converge in the artist's eye. Every point in the picture matches a point in the object being painted.

To help fix these points correctly, mechanical devices were introduced. Among the first was a sighter, to squint through with one eye, and a glass plate held in a frame an arm's length away. The scene could then be outlined on the glass, exactly as it appeared, and afterward traced on the drawing.

A later apparatus, ascribed to Albrecht Dürer, the German painter, used a piece of string as a line of sight. It was pinned to a point on the object, run through an empty frame, and fastened to the eye of a needle driven into the wall. The position of the point where the string intersected the plane of the frame was fixed by two cross threads set in the frame at right angles to each other, like the grid on a piece of graph paper. As the string was pinned successively to key points in the still life, the other end remained fixed to the eye of the needle, so that all the lines converged there, instead of in the artist's eye, leaving him free to move around.

However, no mechanical device could take the place of a knowledge of the mathematical principles involved in this projection of a real scene onto a canvas plane. As Dürer himself wrote, "Geometry is the right foundation of all painting." (This was before the advent of abstract expressionism.) He also understood that perspective was an important branch of mathematics, not just a technique of drawing.

The originator of projective geometry, as such, was a

seventeenth-century architect and engineer, Gerard Desargues. He wrote a book, intended to help artists, which contained the ideas of geometry that are useful in a study of perspective.

A noticeable difference between Euclidean and projective geometry is in their treatment of parallels. In Euclidean geometry parallel lines never meet—they have no point in common. In projective geometry they do. They intersect in what is called an ideal point (similar to the vanishing point in perspective drawing). The set of all points on a line is made up of all the real points, plus an ideal point.

Actually, this is just a change in language. "Two lines are parallel," and "Two lines intersect in an ideal point," say the same thing in different words. It is not meant to imply that the lines *really* meet in a point way off yonder, any more than the railroad tracks do. This mathematical convention is adopted so that in projective geometry you can say any two lines in a plane meet in a point of some sort. Furthermore, all these ideal points lie on the same line—the ideal line. (Think of the horizon, or eye level, line in perspective drawing.)

These geometries are alike in that both are the study of properties which remain invariant under transformation. (So is topology.) The difference is in the kind of transformation. In Euclidean geometry it is rigid motion that moves the figures from place to place without changing their size or shape. Size is a metric property; therefore the geometry of Euclid is a metric geometry. Projection changes both size and shape. The properties that remain invariant are something else. For instance, the projection of a straight line is never curved.

In topology, the transformations are much more drastic. Triangles may become circles, squares may be remolded into decagons. No property of either size, shape, or number of sides is invariant, but a simple closed curve is always a simple closed curve, with one inside and one outside.

PROBLEMS

Solve each of the following problems and classify it as metric or non-metric:

1. A 2-simplex is the union of how many 1-simplexes?
2. A 3-simplex has how many 2-simplexes as faces?
3. Find the volume of a rectangular solid 5 feet long, 4 feet wide, and $2\frac{1}{2}$ feet high.
4. What kind of line—real or ideal—is determined by each of the following sets of points?
   a. 2 real points
   b. 1 real point and 1 ideal point
   c. 2 ideal points
5. What is the area of an equilateral triangle whose side is 3 feet?

12

Coordinate Geometry— The Hybrid Subject

There is a place in the history of mathematics where the twin streams of geometry and algebra come together in a single subject. It happened in France during the seventeenth century with the invention of a method of associating number pairs with points in a plane. The idea is usually credited to René Descartes, a French mathematician of the time, and we call the subject "coordinate geometry," or sometimes "analytical geometry."

As a method for solving problems, algebra and geometry, used separately, each has its advantages and also its limitations. Descartes's invention provided a way of representing an algebraic equation involving x and y by a line (straight or curved) drawn on graph paper. Therefore the best of both algebra and geometry could be brought to bear on a single problem. This method makes possible a world of scientific applications of mathematics—for example, in problems about telescopes, microscopes, searchlights, radio antennae, X-ray machines, and the paths of projectiles of all kinds as well as the paths of planets and comets.

Cartesian Coordinates

The graph devised by Monsieur Descartes is based on the same principle as that used by city planners when they lay out two thoroughfares—say Main Street and Middle Avenue—intersecting at right angles, and then locate everything else as so many blocks east or west of Main Street and north or south of Middle Avenue. The combination of these two pieces of information serves to fix any point. For instance, the location of a building is described by saying it is at the corner of East Second Street and North Third Avenue.

The central idea here is that such a scheme provides a way for showing both the number of blocks and the direction, always starting from a central point. This map also helps to put across the notion that there is a uniform way of marking these directions. It's not important that, by convention, it is north that we put at the top, but it is important that there is a convention regulating this so that we all do it the same way, which makes for ease of communication.

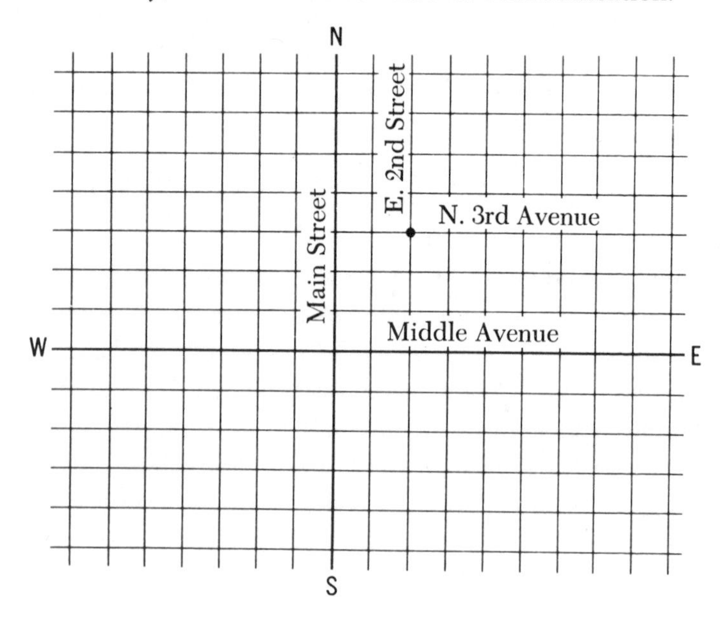

Replace east and west by *X*, north and south by *Y*, and there you have the Cartesian graph. The two thoroughfares are named the *X*-axis (always drawn horizontally) and the *Y*-axis. This layout may not be switched around at will, but is fixed by mathematical convention. A graph with *X* on the vertical axis looks as queer as a map of the United States would if it had Florida sticking up at the top.

The two axes intersect at the zero point, called the origin. Instead of north, south, east, and west, directions are given by using positive and negative numbers, positive being to the right or up, negative to the left or down. (A number with no sign written before it is understood to be positive.)

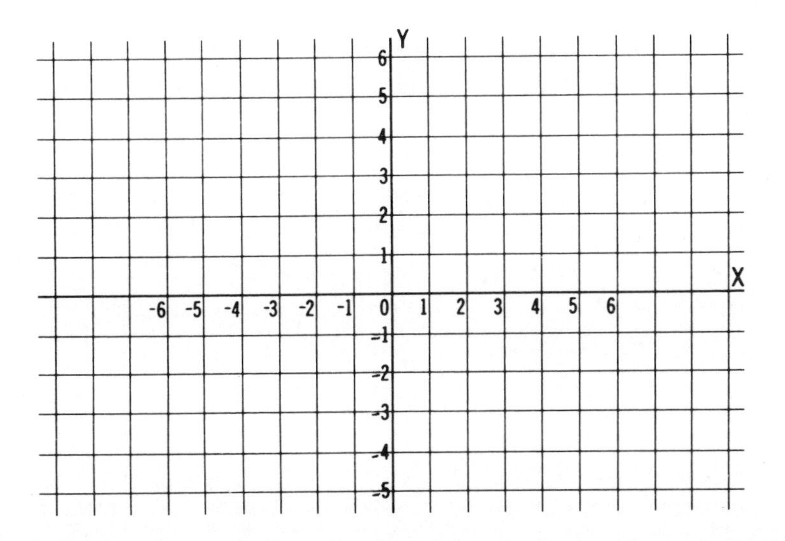

The Cartesian plane is the basis of the subject of analytic geometry. By becoming familiar with it early, so that it becomes a sort of second nature—like reading a map—you get a head start in mathematics and avoid a lot of grief later on.

Graphing an ordered pair of numbers is called "plotting a point," which has a sort of cloak-and-dagger sound, but actually all you do is count squares in the proper directions. For instance, for the pair (2,3) start at the zero point and count two squares to the right and three up, since both numbers are positive. (Count the whole square, landing each time on an intersection of the lines of the grid.) The first number is always counted along the X-axis, the second along the Y-axis. The first number is sometimes called the *abscissa* and the second the *ordinate*. Together they are called the *coordinates*—Cartesian coordinates, to be exact.

Had the pair been (−2,3) you would begin by counting two squares to the left, then three up. It is the sign (positive or negative) which gives you the direction—the numbers tell you how many squares to count. Various combinations of positive and negative 2's and 3's are shown below, as well as some other pairs.

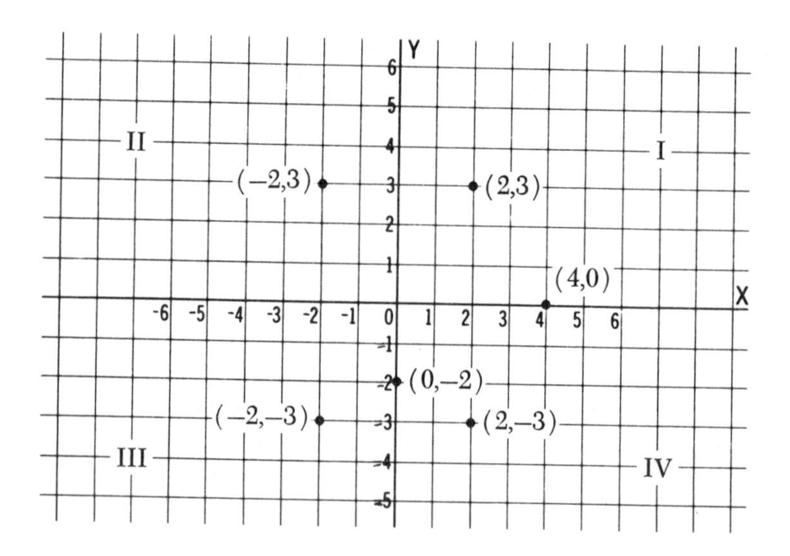

The Roman numerals show the quadrants—i.e., the four quarters into which the X- and Y-axes separate the graph paper. They, too, are always numbered in a fixed way, beginning with the first quadrant on the upper-right-hand side and proceeding in a counterclockwise direction, as you see.

PROBLEMS

1. Plot the following points on a Cartesian graph:
   - a. (3,5)
   - b. (−1,4)
   - c. (3,0)
   - d. (3,−4)
   - e. (2,−1)
   - f. (−5,−3)
   - g. (0,2)

2. What are the coordinates of the points shown on this graph:

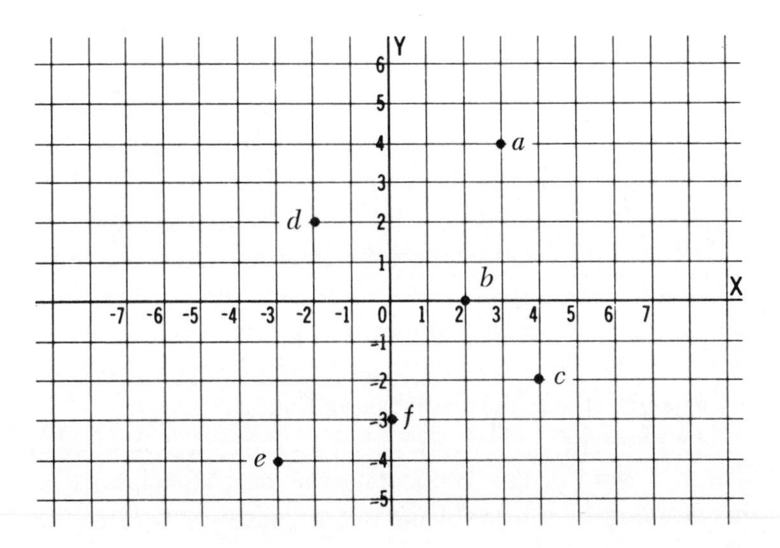

3. In what quadrant are the signs of both numbers in the ordered pair positive? Negative?

Graphs of Discrete and Continuous Cases

Sometimes the dots seem to lie along a straight line. Would it change the meaning of the graph any if you just put a ruler across them and drew in the line? The answer is yes—it certainly would. A series of isolated dots is as different from a line as a ladder, with its separate rungs, is from a ramp. One represents the *discrete* case—the other, the *continuous*.

Discrete objects are objects which can be counted. Maybe you never thought about it, but all the things around us fall into two different categories. You can count the people lounging in the patio, but you can't count the water in the pool. It is continuous, without any breaks.

Man has long gotten around this difficulty by fashioning a measure—say a bucket—and then counting the number of times the measure was filled up. However, it is extremely unlikely that it ever comes out even, to the last drop, no matter how small a bucket is used. All measured quantities are approximate. The smaller the bucket, the closer the approximation, but the measure of a continuous property can never be exact, as the count of discrete objects is.

There is an inherent difference between these two kinds of things. When people enter or leave a group, the count jumps from one whole number to another. There is no in-between. But the water level glides imperceptibly upward as the pool is filled—the change is continuous.

When you are making a graph, how can you tell whether or not to draw a line connecting the dots? Sometimes by the meaning of the problem. But suppose—as is often the case—that the problem contains only symbols. Do we draw in the line or don't we?

The replacement sets for the two variables give the clue (see Chapter Two). If these sets contain only certain explicitly stated numbers, then they are discrete and the graph consists of a series of points with gaps between. For example:

First set: {2,4,6,8}
Second set: {1,2,3,4}

Rule: The first member of each ordered pair is twice the second member.

Arranged in a table, this relation is:

x	y
2	1
4	2
6	3
8	4

Its graph is:

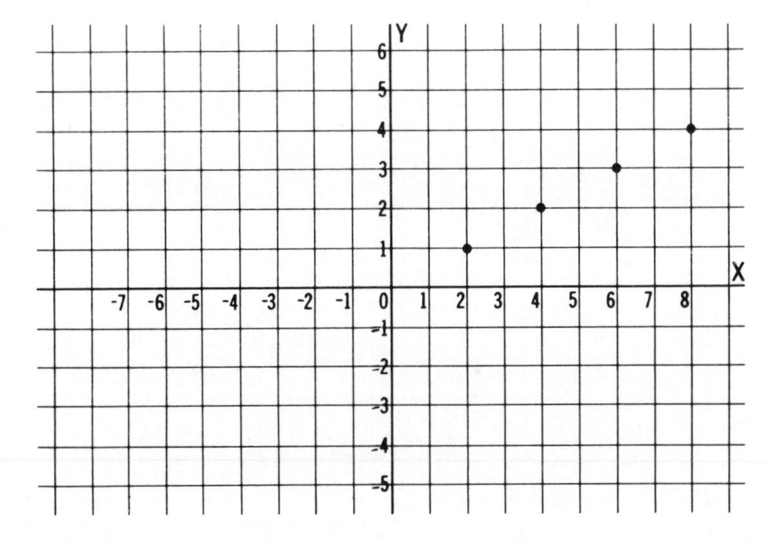

This would still be true, even if the sets were much larger —too large to write all the numbers down and they had to be indicated like this: {1,2,3,4, . . .}. (The three little dots mean to continue counting in the same way indefinitely.) The graph would contain a great many more points, but there would still be gaps between, because there are gaps between these numbers.

On the other hand, suppose the replacement sets had read: {All the real numbers}. (See Chapter Four.) The real number system has no gaps in it. The spaces between the whole numbers are filled with fractions and irrationals—filled up to such an extent that, like water, it is continuous.

However, you don't have to use these exotic numbers in your table. You can use the same table as on page 175, but, after you have located the points, draw a line through them to show that since the replacement sets are continuous, the graph is continuous, too.

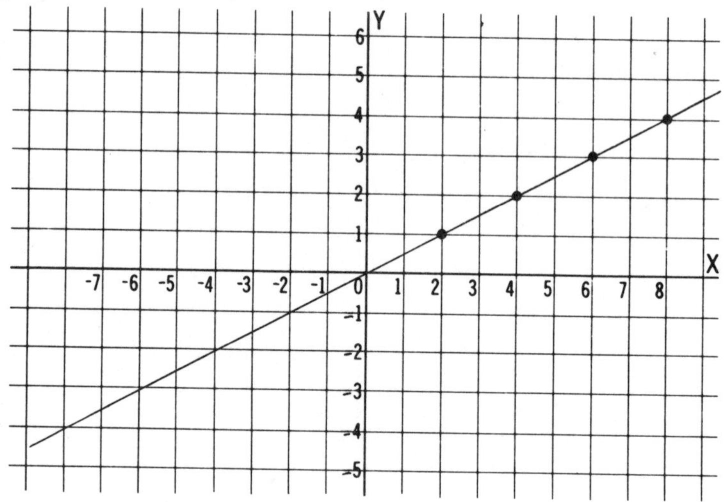

PROBLEMS

Graph the following relations:

1. Rule: The second member of each ordered pair is 2 larger than the first member.
   Replacement set for first variable: {1,2,3,4}
   Replacement set for second variable: {3,4,5,6}

2. Rule: The second member of each ordered pair is 3 less than the first member.
   Replacement sets: {All the real numbers}

Slope

When you look at a group of straight-line graphs, one of the first things you notice is that some rise more steeply than others. Mathematicians call the measure of this steepness the *slope* of the line.

Pretend that you are walking along the *X*-axis, always entering from the left (just as we always read print from the left). If, as you walk along, you come to a line which is going uphill, it has a positive slope. If the line goes downhill, it has a negative slope.

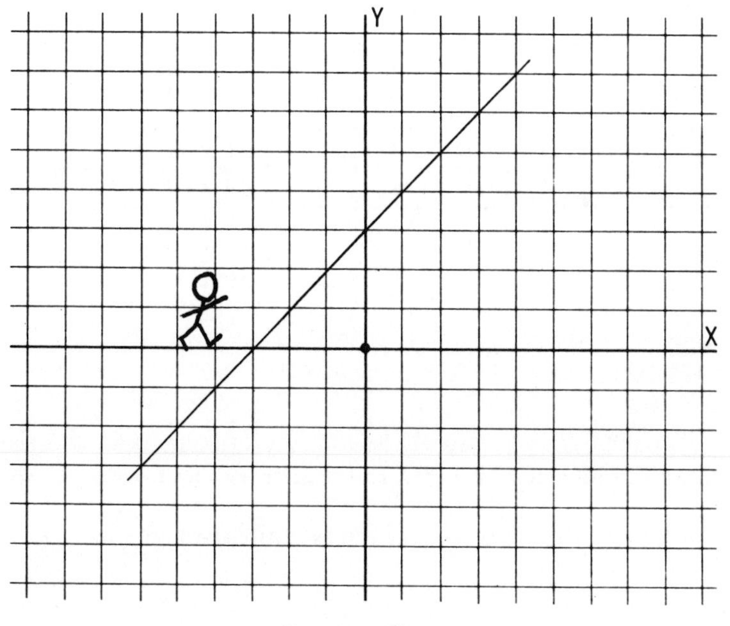

Positive Slope

The slope is a number. It is computed by figuring the ratio of two distances called the *rise* and the *run*. Still pretend you are walking along the X-axis and, beginning at the point where it meets the slanting line of the graph, count the squares as you walk (*run*) from left to right. Then, anywhere you choose, *rise* up in the air, counting squares as you go, until you bump into the slanting line again.

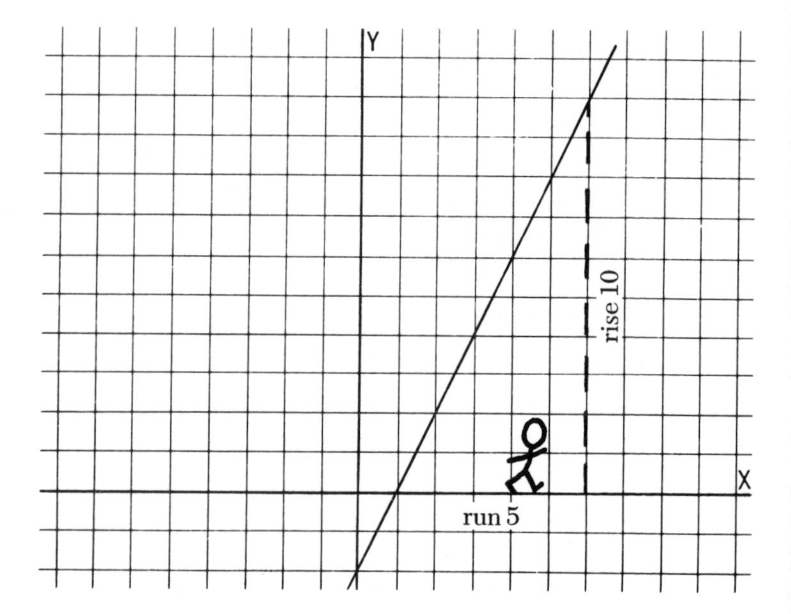

The slope is the ratio of the number of squares in the rise to the number of squares in the run. In the first example, the ratio of rise to run is $\frac{10}{5}$, which is equivalent to $\frac{2}{1}$.

In the case of a line with a negative slope, you see that after you run, you would have to fall in order to bump into the graph line. Mathematically speaking, a fall is represented as a negative rise. The slope of the second line is $\frac{-3}{4}$.

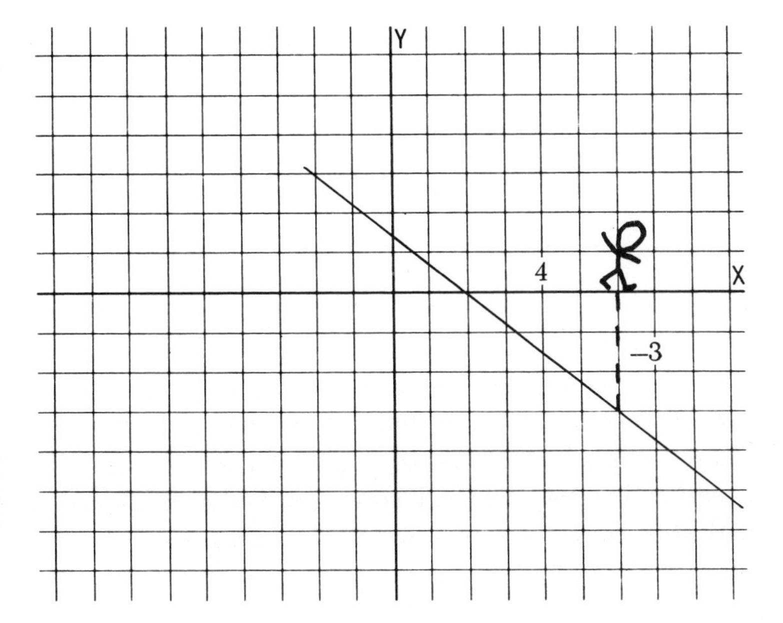

There is a way to predict, in advance, what the slope of a line will be, without drawing the graph. You remember that a relation—a set of ordered pairs—may be expressed as a rule, a formula, a table, or a graph. If you choose to express it as a formula, and this formula is written in a certain way, called the slope-intercept form, the slope jumps right out at you. In the equation $y = 2x + 3$, I see immediately that the rise will be twice the run. The number directly in front of the x tips me off—here it tells me that the slope is 2.

You might wonder how a single figure can be read as a ratio (which must express the relationship between two things). It is because "2" written as the numeral for a ratio really means $\frac{2}{1}$. By custom, when the denominator is 1 we just don't bother to write it. On the other hand, when the 1 is *over* the 2, as in the fraction $\frac{1}{2}$, we do write both numbers. You see 2 written for $\frac{2}{1}$ all the time, but you never see $\frac{}{2}$, meaning $\frac{1}{2}$. Think of pajamas—it's sometimes all right for fractions to go around dressed only in their tops, but never in just their bottoms.

Besides telling me the slope, the formula $y = 2x + 3$ gives me another piece of information about the graph. It tells me where it would cross Main Street, so to speak. The 3 means that the line will cross the Y-axis at the point marked 3. With these two pieces of information, I can, by using what is called the *slope-intercept method*, draw the graph without having to do any of the arithmetic. Find 3 on the Y-axis and, from that point, run 1 square to the right then rise 2 squares and mark the spot. These two points are enough to define the line.

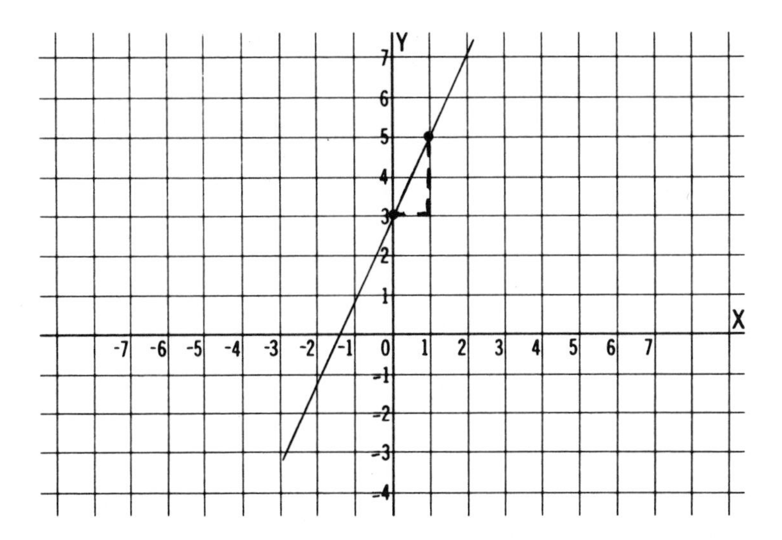

PROBLEMS

1. What would be the slope of each of the following lines if they were graphed? Where would each cross the Y-axis?

   a. $y = \frac{2}{3}x - 6$

   b. $y = -3x + 1$

2. Graph the following by the slope-intercept method:

   $y = 3x + 4$

13

Inequalities and Their Graphs—Lopsided Scales

Equations, I'm sure, are familiar to you, but are you prepared for inequations? Most books say inequalities, but, either way, they look like this: $x + 4 > 6$. The symbol "$>$" means "is greater than." Think of a number which, added to 4, will give a sum greater than 6. Obviously, anything larger than 2 will do. Therefore we have, not one answer, but a set of answers–the solution set. It is written, in the case of the problem above, $x > 2$. Turn "$>$" around and "$<$" means "is less than." (The symbol always points toward the smaller quantity.) If $x + 2 < 7$, the solution set would be $x < 5$.

Equations and inequalities are often presented together–they are both called open sentences. Whether you say: "The ________ won the National League pennant in 1966," or: "____ $+ 9 = 14$" or: "$2 +$ ____ > 5," the idea is the same. Fill in the blank so as to make a true statement. The solution set (also called truth set) of the first sentence is {Dodgers}, of the second, {5} and of the third, {All numbers greater than 3}.

Graphing the Solution Set on a Number Line

The solution to the equation on page 182, which was 5, could be shown on a number line simply by a dot at "5." The solution set of the inequality takes a little more work and looks like this:

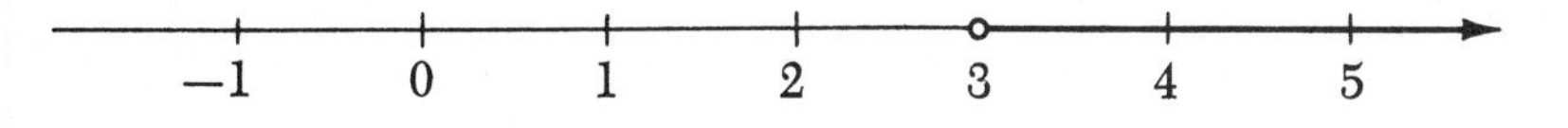

The arrow means that the line continues to the right. The heavily shaded part is the graph of the solution set–the fact that the circle at 3 is left open means that 3 is not included in the set. Only numbers larger than 3, such as 3¼, 4, 4½, etc., will make the open sentence $2 + \underline{\quad\quad} > 5$ true.

If the original problem had read $2 + \underline{\quad\quad} \geqq 5$, meaning that $2 + \underline{\quad\quad}$ was either equal to 5 or greater than 5, then the circle at 3 on the number line would also have been shaded, indicating that the solution set was: {3 and all numbers greater than 3}.

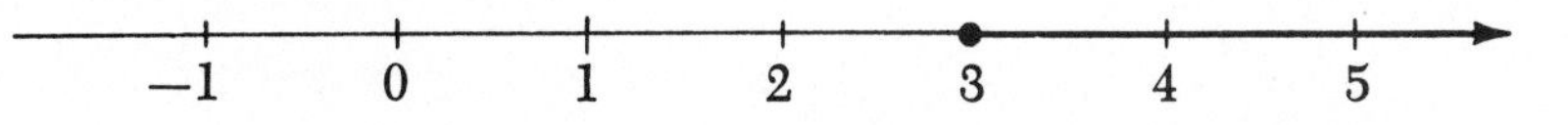

For convenience, *x's* soon replace the blanks. The problem above could just as well have been written $2 + x \geqq 5$, and the solution, $x \geqq 3$.

A more complicated example, like $x^2 > 9$, has a graph in two parts, to match its two-part solution, that x is either greater than 3 or less than −3.

−6 −5 −4 −3 −2 −1 0 1 2 3 4 5 6

A line drawn through the symbol has the effect of inserting a "not" in the wording. $x \not> 5$ says that x is not greater than 5—it is either less than 5 or equal to 5. $x \not\geqq 4$ means that x is not equal to or greater than 4, which is just another (and more complicated) way of saying that it is smaller than 4. A line through the equals sign, as in $x \neq 2$, specifies that x and 2 are unequal, but does not tell you which is larger. Any number, other than 2, would be a solution to the problem.

Some inequalities have no answer at all, for example $8 + x \leqq x$. In that case, the solution is the empty set, and if you are asked to draw a graph, just *don't* draw anything.

PROBLEMS

Find the solution set of each of the following open sentences. Graph the first four on the number line:

1. $x + 5 > 7$
2. $x^2 > 16$
3. $x < -2$
4. $x + 3 \geqq 2$
5. $x \not\geqq -7$
6. $x \geqq x + 6$
7. $2 + 7 \neq x + 2$
8. $x + 4 \not\leqq 8$
9. $x + 5 = 3 + x$
10. $0 \leqq x \leqq 5$

Axioms of Inequalities

In first-year algebra part of the course consists of the theory and practice of solving inequalities, as well as equations. The theory requires certain axioms, or principles of inequality, which are much the same as the axioms of inequality which have always been a part of plane geometry.

One of these is: If the same number is added to both members of an inequality, the results are unequal in the same order. Expressed more compactly in symbols: If $a > b$, then $a + c > b + c$. A numerical example, such as this, makes it obvious:

$$\begin{aligned} 12 &> 5 \\ 12 + 3 &> 5 + 3 \\ 15 &> 8 \end{aligned}$$

Since subtraction can be treated as the addition of an inverse, a separate axiom for subtraction is unnecessary. That is, you can always add a -3 instead of subtracting $+3$, and come out the same. Similarly, you can get around dividing by multiplying by a reciprocal, so there is no need for a separate division axiom, either. The following two axioms for multiplication take care of the matter:

1. If unequal numbers are multiplied by the same *positive* number, the results are unequal in the *same* order.
2. If unequal numbers are multiplied by the same *negative* number, the results are unequal in *reverse* order.

The first part is easy to see.

$$\begin{aligned} 6 &> 4 \\ 2(6) &> 2(4) \\ 12 &> 8 \end{aligned}$$

It's the second part that is tricky.

$$\begin{aligned} 6 &> -1 \\ -2(6) &\ ?\ -2(-1) \\ -12 &\ ?\ 2 \end{aligned}$$

Obviously -12 is not greater than 2; it's less than 2, so the inequality symbol has to be turned around.

These axioms are applied in solving problems in inequalities, such as the following:

1. $2x - 7 > 15$

   $2x > 22$ (Add 7 to both members. Addition Axiom)

   $x > 11$ (Multiply both members by $\frac{1}{2}$. First Multiplication Axiom)

To check your work, take a number greater than 11, such as 12.

$$2(12) - 7 > 15$$
$$24 - 7 > 15$$
$$17 > 15$$

2. $28 - 4x < 8$

   $-4x < -20$ (Add -28 to both members. Addition Axiom)

   $x > 5$ (Multiply both members by $-\frac{1}{4}$. Second Multiplication Axiom. Notice the reversed order of inequality.)

To test your answer, take a number greater than 5, such as 6:

$$28 - 4(6) < 8$$
$$28 - 24 < 8$$
$$4 < 8$$

Look at what would happen if you hadn't turned the inequality sign around and came out with a number smaller than 5. Test 4:

$$28 - 4(4) < 8$$
$$28 - 16 < 8$$
$$12 < 8$$ This is obviously not true.

Problems with the combined symbol "$\geqq$" or "$\leqq$" are worked the same way:

$3x - 2 \leqq 10 - x$

$4x - 2 \leqq 10$ (Add x to each member. Addition Axiom for inequalities)

$4x \leqq 12$ (Add 2 to each member. Addition Axiom for inequalities)

$x \leqq 3$ (Multiply each member by $\frac{1}{4}$. Multiplication Axiom for inequalities)

To check your answer, split it into two parts, $x = 3$, and $x < 3$. For the first part:

$$3(3) - 2 = 10 - (3)$$
$$9 - 2 = 10 - 3$$
$$7 = 7$$

Select a number from the solution set of the second part—for instance, 2:

$$3(2) - 2 < 10 - (2)$$
$$6 - 2 < 10 - 2$$
$$4 < 8$$

PROBLEMS

Solve the following inequalities:

1. $4x - 2 < 10$
2. $x + 5 > 7$
3. $3 + x \leqq 2$
4. $8 - 2x < 14$
5. $6x - 3 < x + 2$
6. $4x + 3 \geqq 7x - 12$

Graphing in a Plane

Just as in equations, you may have inequalities with two variables, x and y, instead of just one. These are most easily analyzed by means of a graph. Since you have two dimensions to picture, a one-dimensional line won't do. It takes a plane—the same Cartesian plane described in Chapter Twelve.

In the problem $x + y > 3$, start by finding out where the line $x + y = 3$ would go on the graph. Make a table of ordered pairs that fit the equation:

x	1	0	2
y	2	3	1

Actually, two pairs are enough, since it only takes two points to determine a straight line. This line separates the points in the plane into three sets—a set of points on the line, a set of points on one side of the line, and a set of points on the other side of the line. The set on the line (the ones in the table above and many others) satisfy the equation. However, we are not graphing it, so make the line dotted. Of the other two sets, one will fit the inequality $x + y > 3$ and the other will fit $x + y < 3$. Your only problem is to decide which is which. Pick a pair of numbers that fulfill the conditions stated in one inequality—for instance, $x = 2$, $y = 4$. Locate that point and see which side of the dotted line it falls on. Try a few more if you want to—they will all fall on the same side of the line. The coordinates of every point in this half plane satisfy the inequality $x + y > 3$, so indicate this fact by shading it in.

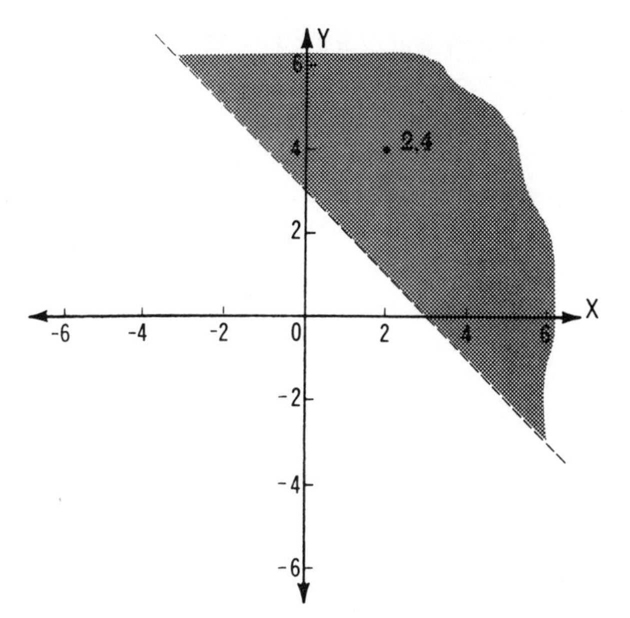

Had you drawn the line solid, instead of dotted, it would show that the points *on* the line were also included in the graph. This would be the case if the problem had been $x + y \geqq 3$.

If several inequalities are graphed simultaneously on the same plane, their common solution will show up in the overlapping of the different shaded areas. This is often a triangle, quadrilateral, or some other polygon, and for that reason is called a polygonal convex set. Linear programming problems (practical problems where certain limitations are placed on the variables) can be solved in this way. Take the following example:

A manufacturer is planning to buy some new machines. There are two models that will fit his needs. He wants at least 2 of Model X and at least 1 of Model Y. His floor space will accommodate only 6 machines. The dealer can supply 4 Model X's and 3 Model Y's. How many of each should he buy for maximum output, if Model X can manufacture 600 gadgets a day and Model Y can manufacture 500 gadgets a day?

From the conditions given you can set up the inequalities, letting $x =$ the number of Model X machines he should buy, and $y =$ the number of Model Y's. Since he will buy at least 2 of Model X, then x either equals 2 or is greater than 2. Write this in symbols as:

$$x \geqq 2$$

Similarly, because he will buy at least 1 of Model Y:

$$y \geqq 1$$

Graph each of these two inequalities by the method explained above, putting them both on the same plane.

You also know that the sum of the two models will be 6 or less, because the floor space will only accommodate that many. Express this algebraically as:

$$x + y \leqq 6$$

and graph it on the same plane as the other two.

The conditions about the number the dealer can supply give you the facts that the number of Model X's must be 4 or less, written as:

$$x \leqq 4$$

and the number of Model Y's is 3 or less, written:

$$y \leqq 3$$

Graph these two inequalities also on the same plane and you have this:

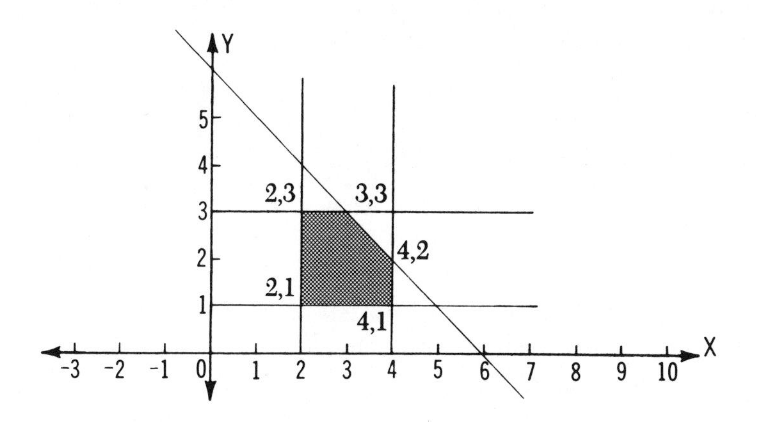

For purposes of clarification I have shaded in only the overlapping areas—otherwise there would be a welter of five different kinds of cross-hatching, one to go with each of the five lines graphed. Any point in this shaded region or on its boundaries represents a pair of numbers that will fit the conditions laid down in the problem. The question now is: Which one of these pairs will give the manufacturer maximum output?

It can be proved (but beyond the scope of this book) that the maximum occurs at a vertex of the polygon, therefore the answer will be one of the five number pairs which you see at the vertices of the figure on the graph above. Bearing in mind that in graphing the x is always named first, you now know that the five possibilities are: 2 Model *X* machines and 3 Model *Y;* 3 Model *X* and 3 Model *Y;* 4 Model *X* and 2 Model *Y;* etc.

Test these five possibilities by multiplying, in each case, the number of machines by the number of gadgets it can produce in a day, which the problem tells you is 600 for Model X and 500 for Model Y.

$$\begin{aligned}
600(2) + 500(3) &= 1200 + 1500 = 2700 \\
600(3) + 500(3) &= 1800 + 1500 = 3300 \\
600(4) + 500(2) &= 2400 + 1000 = 3400 \\
600(4) + 500(1) &= 2400 + 500 = 2900 \\
600(2) + 500(1) &= 1200 + 500 = 1700
\end{aligned}$$

You see that the third pair tested gives the largest value. Therefore, the manufacturer should buy 4 Model X machines and 2 Model Y.

While this example is simple enough so that you could guess the answer without going through all the steps, in actual practice linear programming problems generally require computer solution because of their size.

PROBLEMS

Joe, a college student, takes two courses that require a lot of time—Esperanto and Early Egyptian plumbing. (The rest of his schedule is a snap.) The Esperanto department requires that at least 5 hours a week be spent in the language laboratory, which is open from 2:00 to 5:00 o'clock Monday through Friday, inclusive. An enterprising former student has figured out that, on the average, each hour spent per week in the lab adds 5 points to the grade in the course. The Egyptian Museum's rare specimen room is open from 2:00 until 4:00 o'clock on Monday, Wednesday, and Saturday. Mr. Cxyzptv, who teaches Early Egyp. Plumb., estimates that each half-hour per week spent there is worth 4 points on a student's grade. If Joe, after allowing time for his necessities, duties, and pleasures, has a total of 17 hours a week to spend on the two courses, how can he best divide his time between them in order to secure maximum returns for his work?

PART V

14

Vectors—They Went Thataway

If you read, "The getaway car was traveling east at 80 miles per hour," you are looking at an example of a *vector quantity*, which mathematicians define as a quantity having both magnitude and direction. It is usually pictured as an arrow, like this: ⟶. The length of the shaft is drawn proportional to the magnitude—longer if the speed were 90 miles per hour, shorter for 70. The arrow tip points toward the direction in which the car is moving. Other examples of vector quantities are: a pull of 150 pounds acting downward; a motion of 10 miles from point A to point B.

The study of vectors has come to the fore in this age of aerospace technology with its attendant problems involving motion, velocity, and force. In describing the course of an airplane (to say nothing of a spaceship), both the speed and direction are essential. And what happens when two vector quantities conflict? For example, an airplane's engines are driving it eastward at what would be 500 miles per hour in still air, but a 50-mile-an-hour wind from the north is pushing it sideways. Where will this plane actually go? A knowledge of the way vectors interact will give the answer. Similarly, in space travel there is the whole complex of rocket's thrust versus the gravitational pull exerted by the earth, moon, planets, etc. Each of these forces has both magnitude and direction.

Scalars and Vectors

A quantity that has magnitude only (such as a rope 15 feet long) is called in mathematical parlance a *scalar*. Scalar quantities carry no sense of direction. They are measured merely by counting units—inches, pounds, days, apples, people, etc. Even when motion is implied, as in 80 miles per hour, this just tells you that the unit of measure is miles per hour and there are 80 of them. You know nothing about the direction this motion takes.

In geometry, a line segment connecting points A and B is named AB. BA would do just as well, since the distance between the two points is the same, no matter which end you measure from. But in vector notation, to show that the idea of direction is involved, a little arrow is placed over the letters, like this: $\overrightarrow{AB}$. Not only does this symbol refer to the distance between points A and B (let's call them Albany and Baltimore), but it also indicates that someone, or something, is moving *from* Albany *to* Baltimore. Motion in the opposite direction—i.e., from Baltimore to Albany—is symbolized by $\overrightarrow{BA}$. These two things are not the same at all. In the first case a plane would be heading toward the Gulf of Mexico, in the second, toward Canada. $\overrightarrow{AB}$ does not equal

$\overrightarrow{BA}$. Vectors, to be equal, must not only be the same length, but must also have the same direction.

On a drawing, direction may be shown by the map-makers' familiar convention of putting north at the top of the page. Thus in the line at the beginning of this chapter, motion due east is depicted by pointing the arrow straight to the right. Other examples are:

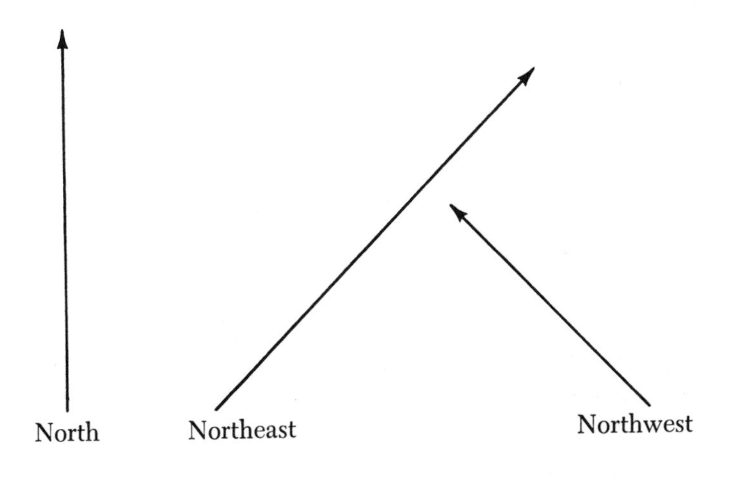

These are all scale drawings, with the length of the line in proportion to the size of the vector. I arbitrarily chose a scale of 1 inch to represent a speed of 40 miles per hour. The first figure shows a speed of 80 miles per hour due north; the second, 100 miles an hour northeast; the third, 60 miles an hour toward the northwest.

An alternate method of describing direction—instead of using north, east, south, and west—is to give the angle that the vector makes with a fixed line, usually horizontal. In this system, the drawings above would look like this:

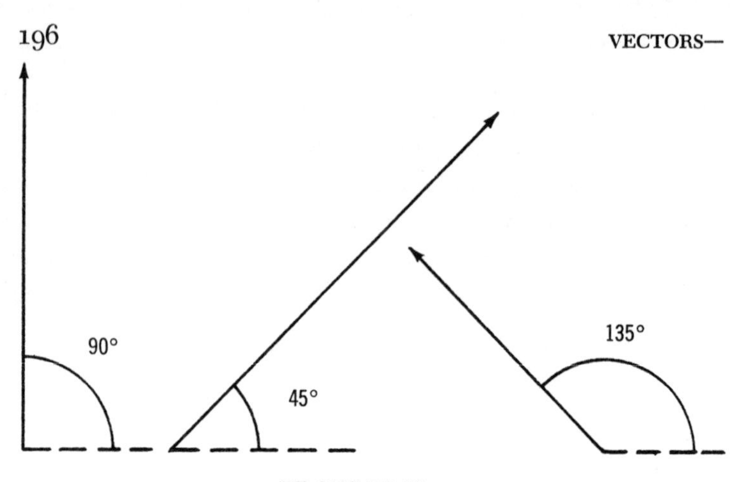

PROBLEMS

1. Which of the following are scalars and which are vectors:
   a. 12 years of age
   b. A speed of 300 miles per hour due west
   c. A population of 500,000
   d. 48 hours
   e. A river current flowing 4 miles per hour toward the southeast
2. Using the terms of north, east, south, and west, how would you describe the directions indicated by the following drawings?

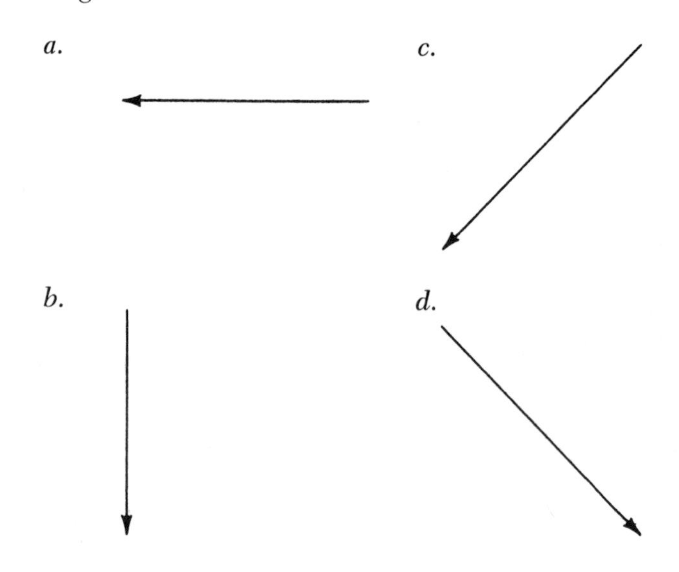

Vector Addition

When vectors are added, the sum may be different from what you would expect. That is because "add" is used, not in its strict arithmetical sense, but more as a cookbook does when the recipe tells you to "add a teaspoon of salt." The meaning, really, is to combine the vectors. Their sum is the end result of the combination of forces and directions represented by the vectors.

For example, consider that getaway car at the beginning of this chapter. Suppose it travels 80 miles due east, then turns north for the next 60 miles. What is the vector sum of the two motions—i.e., how far from the scene of the crime is the car now and in what direction?

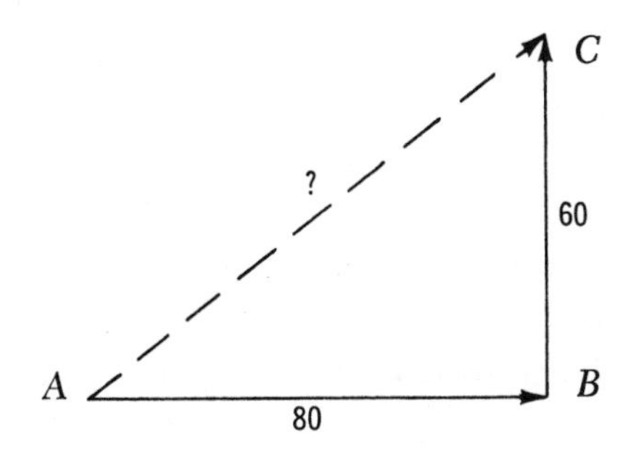

Since the final result of the two movements is the same as if the car had driven directly from A to C, we can write in symbols: $\overrightarrow{AB} + \overrightarrow{BC} = \overrightarrow{AC}$. To solve the problem requires finding the size and direction of vector $\overrightarrow{AC}$. There are several ways to do this. One is to make a scale drawing, constructing a 90° angle at B. (The handiest way is with a protractor

—a plastic semicircle marked off in degrees from 0 to 180, which you can get at the dime store.)

Now measure $\overrightarrow{AC}$ with a ruler and, using the scale, convert it to miles. For example, if the diagram is drawn to the scale of 1 inch = 40 miles, then:

$\overrightarrow{AB} = 80$ miles $= 2$ inches*
$\overrightarrow{BC} = 60$ miles $= 1\frac{1}{2}$ inches
$\overrightarrow{AC}$ measures $2\frac{1}{2}$ inches
$2\frac{1}{2} \times 40 = 100$

Therefore the car is 100 miles from its starting point. Here the vector sum of 80 and 60 is 100, not 140 as in arithmetic. Looking at the diagram, you can see that 140 would not be a reasonable answer to this problem, since a line directly from *A* to *C* is bound to be shorter than one which detours by way of *B*.

C is in a general northeasterly direction from *A*, which information will probably be accurate enough for the sheriff to find it, but if you want to be mathematically precise, use your protractor to measure the angle at *A*, and describe the direction of vector $\overrightarrow{AC}$ by saying it makes a 37° angle with the horizontal.

If you would rather not go through the somewhat tedious work of constructing a scale drawing, there is another way of finding the size of $\overrightarrow{AC}$. It utilizes a famous theorem credited to Pythagoras, who discovered that, in any right

*In these equations, $\overrightarrow{AB}$ is understood to mean the *length* of $\overrightarrow{AB}$.

triangle, the square of the length of the hypotenuse equals the sum of the squares of the lengths of the two legs. Condensed, this means:

$$\text{leg}^2 + \text{leg}^2 = \text{hypotenuse}^2$$

The legs are the two sides which form the right angle. Some books, with Victorian delicacy, call them arms. At any rate, the limbs squared and added equal the hypotenuse squared. (The hypotenuse is the side opposite the right angle.) Following this method:

$$\begin{aligned} (\overrightarrow{AB})^2 + (\overrightarrow{BC})^2 &= (\overrightarrow{AC})^2 \\ 80^2 + 60^2 &= (\overrightarrow{AC})^2 \\ 6400 + 3600 &= (\overrightarrow{AC})^2 \\ 10{,}000 &= (\overrightarrow{AC})^2 \\ 100 &= \overrightarrow{AC} \end{aligned}$$

Another example of a problem using vectors is this: A ball lying on a playing field is hit simultaneously by two forces. One, with a strength of 30 pounds, is driving it toward the east; the other, a 40-pound force, is pushing it toward the north. What will happen to the ball?

Assembling the vectors into a diagram, we have:

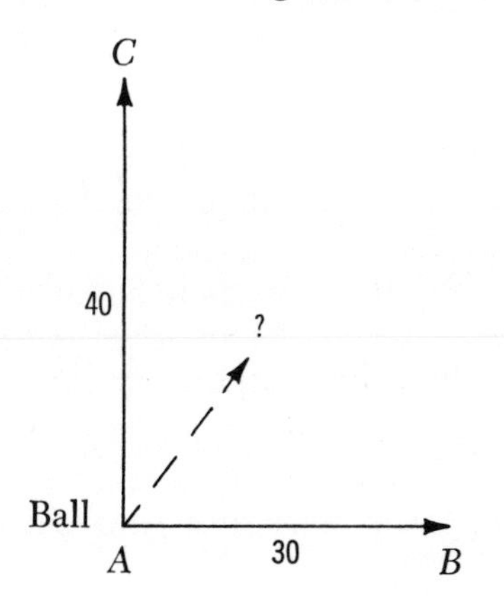

Common sense tells you that the ball will go somewhere in between the two forces, but exactly where? When two forces act on a body at the same point, the effect is just as if it were acted on by a single force which is the *sum* of the two. The *vector sum*, that is, because common sense also tells you that merely adding 30 and 40 will not work. The two forces are acting at cross-purposes and therefore partially cancel each other out.

What is called in physics the *parallelogram law of forces* gives the answer. Draw two more lines on the diagram, one parallel to $\overrightarrow{AB}$ and the other parallel to $\overrightarrow{AC}$.

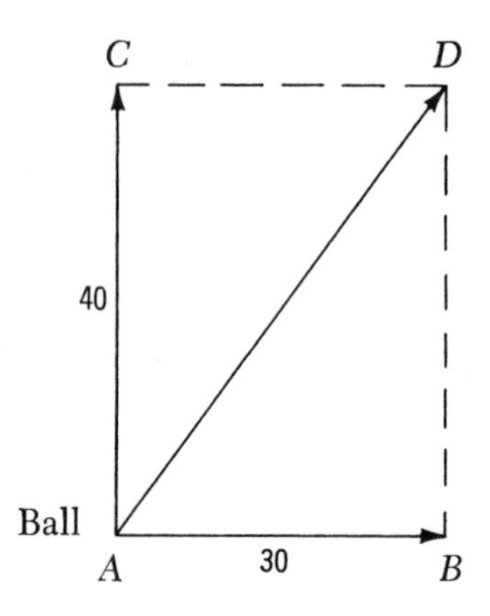

The line from A to D, the opposite corner of the parallelogram, represents the result of combining the two vectors, $\overrightarrow{AB}$ and $\overrightarrow{AC}$. For this reason it is called the *resultant;* $\overrightarrow{AB}$ and $\overrightarrow{AC}$ are called the *components.* $\overrightarrow{AD}$ is the vector sum of $\overrightarrow{AB}$ and $\overrightarrow{AC}$.

Since the opposite sides of a parallelogram are equal, BD

is the same length as *AC* and may be substituted for it. The problem then resolves itself into a right triangle, just like the example about the getaway car, and can be solved in the same two ways—either by a scale drawing or by the Pythagorean Theorem.

$$
\begin{aligned}
(\overrightarrow{AB})^2 + (\overrightarrow{BD})^2 &= (\overrightarrow{AD})^2 \\
30^2 + 40^2 &= (\overrightarrow{AD})^2 \\
900 + 1600 &= (\overrightarrow{AD})^2 \\
2500 &= (\overrightarrow{AD})^2 \\
50 &= \overrightarrow{AD}
\end{aligned}
$$

The ball will behave as if hit by a single force of 50 pounds and will move along a path making an angle of approximately 53° with *AB*, as you can tell by measuring the lower angle at *A* with your protractor.

Notice that in both these examples the two given forces were acting at right angles with each other. What happens when they are not? The scale-drawing method of solution will still work, but the Pythagorean Theorem will not, because it applies only to right triangles. In other kinds of triangles, the missing side must be found by trigonometry.

PROBLEMS

1. A camping party hikes 12 miles due south from a village, then goes 5 miles due east and pitches a tent. How far from the village is the campsite, as the crow flies?
2. A boat that can move at 8 miles per hour in still water is heading across a river from one bank to a point directly opposite on the other bank. At the same time, a river current of 6 miles per hour is pushing against the side of the boat at right angles to it. How fast will the boat actually go?

3. Two forces, one with a strength of 3 pounds and the other with a strength of 4 pounds, are simultaneously pulling at an object. If the two forces are acting at right angles to each other, what is the resultant?

Vectors as Ordered Pairs

An important characteristic of new math is the desire to develop mathematics as a unified structure. In the past, a student often studied one topic until he passed a test on it, then locked that knowledge up in a compartment in his brain and threw away the key. Today the trend is to stress the way that the different parts of mathematics fit together so that you can see the whole vista.

Vectors provide a connecting link between several branches of mathematics. For example, look at the diagram below which shows, side by side, a Cartesian coordinate system like the ones in Chapter Twelve and a drawing of a vector.

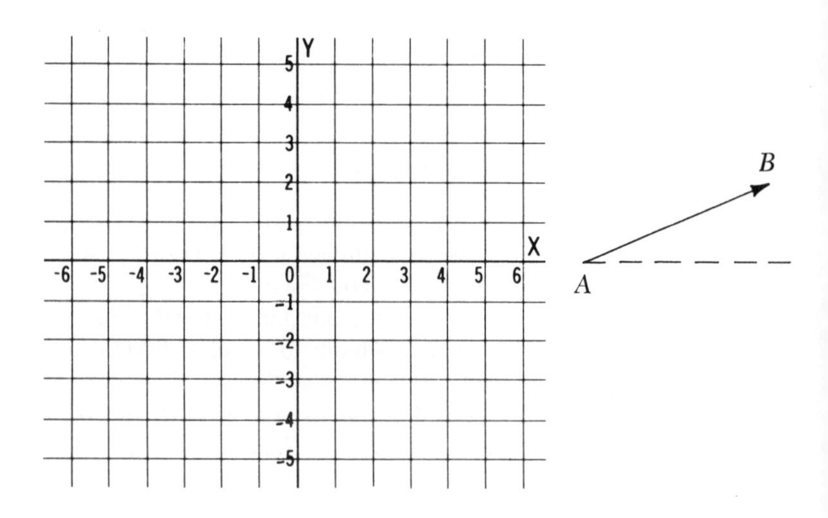

Now superimpose the vector on the graph paper, fitting the horizontal dotted line of the drawing along the positive side of the X-axis.

Instead of a *free vector* whose starting point, A, can be anywhere, we now have a *centered vector* which always begins at the origin (zero point) of a Cartesian coordinate system and then moves in the direction specified by the conditions of the problem. Notice that the tip of the arrow falls on a point on the graph paper. That point corresponds to an ordered pair of numbers, as explained in Chapter Twelve—in this case it is the ordered pair (5,2).

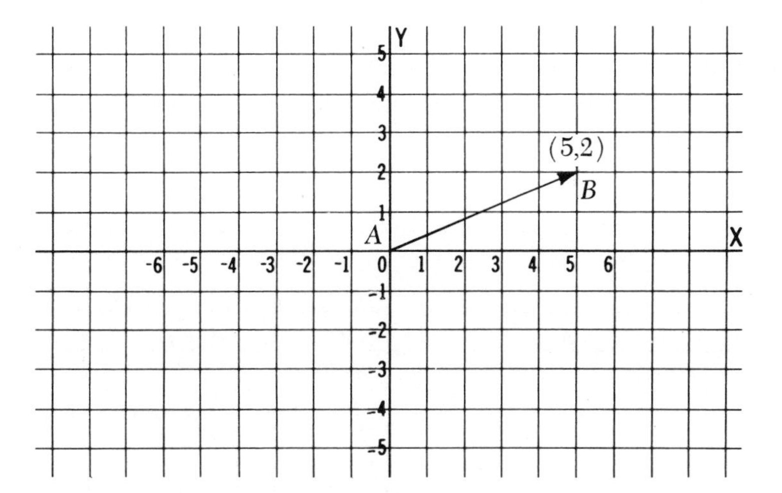

Therefore, instead of describing the direction of vector $\overrightarrow{AB}$ in terms of north and east or by giving the number of degrees in the angle it makes with the horizontal, the ordered pair (5,2) suffices to locate it exactly. You know instantly that the vector can be represented by a line segment on the graph from (0,0) to (5,2). Furthermore, graph paper provides a ready-made scale, eliminating the need for the tedious work of making a scale drawing to show $\overrightarrow{AB}$ in its proper length.

Identifying vectors with ordered pairs of numbers turns out to be very advantageous. It enables us to find a vector sum by simply adding the coordinates. To take another example, if

$$\overrightarrow{OB} = (5,2)$$

and $$\overrightarrow{OA} = (1,3)$$

then $$\overrightarrow{OB} + \overrightarrow{OA} = (6,5)$$

Shown on a diagram and using the parallelogram law of forces, the resultant does, indeed, exactly reach to the point (6,5).

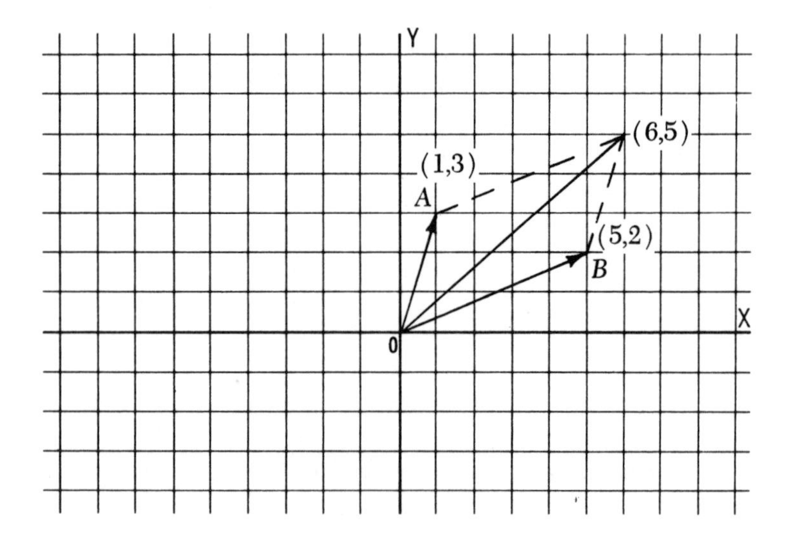

Another operation often performed on vectors is to multiply them by a scalar—i.e., by a single number. Expressing the vector as an ordered pair facilitates the work here, too. Suppose the arrow representing vector $\overrightarrow{OA}$ reaches to the point (2,3). If vector $\overrightarrow{OA}$ is multiplied by 2, the arrow is stretched out to twice its original length and now reaches the point (4,6).

This answer could have been predicted by merely multiplying (2,3) by 2. In the same way, $3\ \overrightarrow{OA} = (6,9)$ and $4\ \overrightarrow{OA} = (8,12)$. Notice that, although the length of the vector is doubled, or tripled, or quadrupled, the direction remains unchanged.

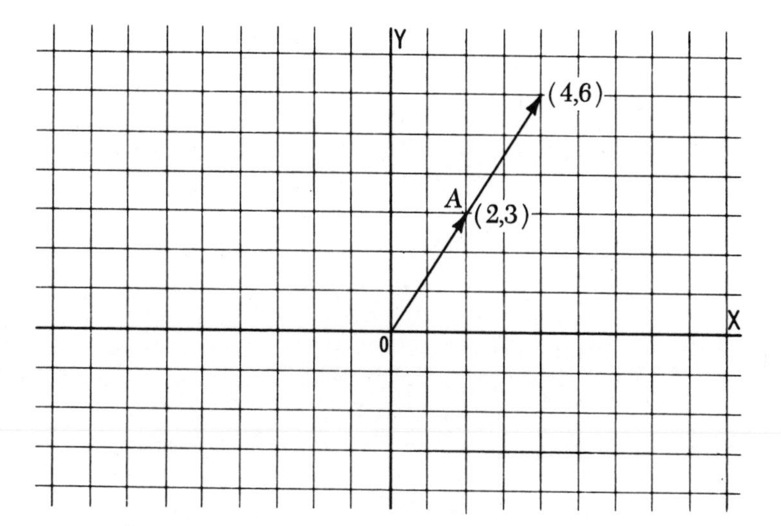

PROBLEMS

If the terminal point of $\overrightarrow{OA}$ is (1,3) and the terminal point of $\overrightarrow{OB}$ is (2,4), find each of the following:

1. $\overrightarrow{OA} + \overrightarrow{OB}$
2. $2\ \overrightarrow{OA}$
3. $3\ \overrightarrow{OB}$
4. $\overrightarrow{OA} + 2\ \overrightarrow{OB}$

15

Matrices—Rows and Columns

Matrices provide a very powerful condensed language in which complicated mathematical statements can be expressed simply. Computations for rocket and projectile flight use matrices. They are an indispensable tool in atomic physics, electrical engineering, statistics, and modern economic theory. A great number of the operations performed by giant computers involve matrices.

A matrix (singular of matrices) is a rectangular array of entries (usually numerals) lined up in rows and columns, such as:

$$\begin{pmatrix} 5 & 1 & 2 \\ 1 & 4 & 0 \\ 6 & 3 & 4 \end{pmatrix}$$

This is a square matrix, 3 by 3, but any rectangular arrangement is possible. You can have 2 by 3 matrices, 1 by 4 matrices, 4 by 2 matrices, and so on. (The number of rows is always written first and then the number of columns.) Here is a 2 by 3 matrix:

$$\begin{pmatrix} 1 & 6 & 5 \\ 2 & 3 & 4 \end{pmatrix}$$

A 3 by 2 would look like this:

$$\begin{pmatrix} 0 & 1 \\ 7 & 4 \\ 2 & 5 \end{pmatrix}$$

The vectors which you saw described in Chapter Fourteen could be written in the form of 1 by 2 matrices. For example:

$$\begin{pmatrix} 5 & 2 \end{pmatrix}$$

Operations with Matrices

The first thing to understand when working with matrices is that a change in the position of the entries makes a difference. These two matrices are not the same, even though they contain the same numbers.

$$\begin{pmatrix} 1 & 3 \\ 2 & 4 \end{pmatrix} \qquad \begin{pmatrix} 3 & 1 \\ 2 & 4 \end{pmatrix}$$

Two matrices are equal only if each entry in one is equal to the corresponding entry in the other. The two examples above are not equal, but these are:

$$\begin{pmatrix} 1 & 3 \\ 2 & 4 \end{pmatrix} = \begin{pmatrix} 4/4 & \sqrt{9} \\ 6/3 & 2 \times 2 \end{pmatrix}$$

Furthermore, matrices, to be equal, must have the same dimensions. A 2 by 2 matrix cannot equal a 2 by 3 matrix, even if it is filled in with zeros.

$$\begin{pmatrix} 1 & 3 \\ 2 & 4 \end{pmatrix} \text{ does not equal } \begin{pmatrix} 1 & 3 & 0 \\ 2 & 4 & 0 \end{pmatrix}$$

Addition is performed exactly the way you would expect. Add each number in one matrix to its mate at the corresponding position in the other matrix and write the sum in that same position in the answer.

$$\begin{pmatrix} 1 & 3 \\ 2 & 4 \end{pmatrix} + \begin{pmatrix} 2 & 4 \\ 6 & 1 \end{pmatrix} = \begin{pmatrix} 3 & 7 \\ 8 & 5 \end{pmatrix}$$

Only matrices with like dimensions can be added.

$$\begin{pmatrix} 1 & 3 \\ 2 & 4 \end{pmatrix} + \begin{pmatrix} 2 & 4 \\ 6 & 1 \\ 0 & 0 \end{pmatrix} \text{ does not equal } \begin{pmatrix} 3 & 7 \\ 8 & 5 \\ 0 & 0 \end{pmatrix}$$

These two matrices cannot be added at all, since one is a 2 by 2 and the other a 3 by 2. Similarly, (0)—a 1 by 1 matrix—cannot be added to a matrix with different dimensions.

$$\begin{pmatrix} 1 & 3 \\ 2 & 4 \end{pmatrix} + (0) \text{ does not equal } \begin{pmatrix} 1 & 3 \\ 2 & 4 \end{pmatrix}$$

If you are looking for the identity element for addition—a matrix that behaves the way 0 does in ordinary addition—it has to be a matrix made up of zeros, but having the same dimensions as the matrix you wish to add it to.

$$\begin{pmatrix} 1 & 3 \\ 2 & 4 \end{pmatrix} + \begin{pmatrix} 0 & 0 \\ 0 & 0 \end{pmatrix} = \begin{pmatrix} 1 & 3 \\ 2 & 4 \end{pmatrix}$$

Adding a matrix to itself, as in this example:

$$\begin{pmatrix} 3 & 1 \\ 5 & 6 \end{pmatrix} + \begin{pmatrix} 3 & 1 \\ 5 & 6 \end{pmatrix} = \begin{pmatrix} 6 & 2 \\ 10 & 12 \end{pmatrix}$$

could be written more compactly as:

$$2 \begin{pmatrix} 3 & 1 \\ 5 & 6 \end{pmatrix} = \begin{pmatrix} 6 & 2 \\ 10 & 12 \end{pmatrix}$$

Here 2 is a number and is written without parentheses, to show that it is not a 1 by 1 matrix. Multiplication of a matrix by a number (called a scalar) turns out just as you probably would predict. It simply multiplies every entry in the matrix by that number.

Multiplication of a matrix by a matrix is considerably more complicated. If you guessed that you merely multiply each pair of corresponding entries together, you are wrong.

It works like this: Take each entry in a *row* of the first matrix and multiply it by the corresponding entry in a fixed *column* of the second matrix. In other words—first row, second entry times first column, second entry. So far, in the problem

$$\begin{pmatrix} 3 & 1 \\ 5 & 6 \end{pmatrix} \times \begin{pmatrix} 4 & 2 \\ 7 & 8 \end{pmatrix}$$ you have $3 \times 4 = 12$, and $1 \times 7 = 7$.

Add these two products $(12 + 7 = 19)$ and write the sum in the first row, first column of your answer.

$$\begin{pmatrix} 19 & - \\ - & - \end{pmatrix}$$

Now do the same thing for the first row of the first matrix and the *second* column of the second matrix. $3 \times 2 = 6$, and $1 \times 8 = 8$. Add these two products $(6 + 8 = 14)$ and fill in the proper spot in your answer.

$$\begin{pmatrix} 19 & 14 \\ - & - \end{pmatrix}$$

Repeat the procedure with the second row of the first matrix and the first column of the other matrix. $5 \times 4 = 20$, and $6 \times 7 = 42$. Take the sum $(20 + 42 = 62)$ and write it in where it belongs.

$$\begin{pmatrix} 19 & 14 \\ 62 & - \end{pmatrix}$$

Finish up with $5 \times 2 = 10$, and $6 \times 8 = 48$. Add 10 and 48 and write 58 in your answer.

$$\begin{pmatrix} 19 & 14 \\ 62 & 58 \end{pmatrix}$$

The two matrices in this problem are both 2 by 2's. Can matrices with different dimensions be multiplied, or—like addition—do they have to be alike? The answer is that they have to partially match. The number of columns of the first must be the same as the number of rows of the second. For instance, you can multiply a 1 by 3 matrix by a 3 by 1 matrix, such as this:

$$(5 \quad 1 \quad 2) \times \begin{pmatrix} 0 \\ 4 \\ 1 \end{pmatrix} = (6)$$

First row, first column $(5 \times 0) + (1 \times 4) + (2 \times 1) =$
$0 + 4 + 2 = 6.$

But you couldn't take a 1 by 3 times a 2 by 1.

$$(5 \quad 1 \quad 2) \times \begin{pmatrix} 0 \\ 4 \end{pmatrix}$$

If you try, you get: first row, first column $(5 \times 0) + (1 \times 4) + (2 \times \_\_)$. You see that there is nothing to multiply the 2—the last entry of the row—by. Therefore, multiplication is impossible in such a case.

If you study the structure of matrix algebra as a mathematical system (see Chapter Six), the question of identity elements for addition and multiplication comes up. We found the additive identity, or zero matrix, a few pages back, but is there a matrix that plays the same role as 1 in ordinary multiplication? A logical guess would be a matrix in which every entry is 1, but if you try an example you see it doesn't work.

$$\begin{pmatrix} 1 & 2 \\ 3 & 4 \end{pmatrix} \times \begin{pmatrix} 1 & 1 \\ 1 & 1 \end{pmatrix} = \begin{pmatrix} 3 & 3 \\ 7 & 7 \end{pmatrix}$$

First row, first column $(1 \times 1) + (2 \times 1) =$
$1 + 2 = 3$
First row, second column $(1 \times 1) + (2 \times 1) =$
$1 + 2 = 3$
Second row, first column $(3 \times 1) + (4 \times 1) =$
$3 + 4 = 7$
Second row, second column $(3 \times 1) + (4 \times 1) =$
$3 + 4 = 7$

The answer is certainly not identical with the first matrix. Here is the special matrix that acts like 1.

$$\begin{pmatrix} 1 & 2 \\ 3 & 4 \end{pmatrix} \times \begin{pmatrix} 1 & 0 \\ 0 & 1 \end{pmatrix} = \begin{pmatrix} 1 & 2 \\ 3 & 4 \end{pmatrix}$$

First row, first column $(1 \times 1) + (2 \times 0) = 1$
First row, second column $(1 \times 0) + (2 \times 1) =$
$0 + 2 = 2$
Second row, first column $(3 \times 1) + (4 \times 0) =$
$3 + 0 = 3$
Second row, second column $(3 \times 0) + (4 \times 1) =$
$0 + 4 = 4$

Another question in the study of the structure of matrix algebra is: Does its multiplication obey the law of commutation? (See Chapter Six). Is Matrix *A* times Matrix *B* the same as Matrix *B* times Matrix *A*? Go back to the first problem we did in matrix multiplication, which was:

$$\begin{pmatrix} 3 & 1 \\ 5 & 6 \end{pmatrix} \times \begin{pmatrix} 4 & 2 \\ 7 & 8 \end{pmatrix} = \begin{pmatrix} 19 & 14 \\ 62 & 58 \end{pmatrix}$$

Now try it reversed and you, too, may DISCOVER something.

$$\begin{pmatrix} 4 & 2 \\ 7 & 8 \end{pmatrix} \times \begin{pmatrix} 3 & 1 \\ 5 & 6 \end{pmatrix}$$

First row, first column $(4 \times 3) + (2 \times 5) = 12 + 10 = 22$

First row, second column $(4 \times 1) + (2 \times 6) = 4 + 12 = 16$

Second row, first column $(7 \times 3) + (8 \times 5) = 21 + 40 = 61$

Second row, second column $(7 \times 1) + (8 \times 6) = 7 + 48 = 55$

Did you get the same answer you did the first time? I didn't. I got:

$$\begin{pmatrix} 4 & 2 \\ 7 & 8 \end{pmatrix} \times \begin{pmatrix} 3 & 1 \\ 5 & 6 \end{pmatrix} = \begin{pmatrix} 22 & 16 \\ 61 & 55 \end{pmatrix}$$

Therefore, matrix multiplication, unlike multiplication in ordinary arithmetic, is not a commutative operation.

PROBLEMS

1. Find the value of x and y:

$$\begin{pmatrix} 1 & 2 & 3 \\ 4 & 6 & 7 \\ 5 & 8 & 9 \end{pmatrix} = \begin{pmatrix} 1 & 2 & y/3 \\ 2x & 6 & 7 \\ 5 & 8 & 9 \end{pmatrix}$$

Perform the following computations, where possible:

2. $$\begin{pmatrix} 1 & 7 \\ 5 & 2 \end{pmatrix} + \begin{pmatrix} 3 & 6 \\ 1 & 4 \end{pmatrix}$$

3. $$2 \times \begin{pmatrix} 6 & 3 \\ 5 & 4 \end{pmatrix}$$

4. $$\begin{pmatrix} 4 & 2 & 5 \\ 6 & 3 & 0 \end{pmatrix} + \begin{pmatrix} 2 & -3 \\ 5 & 7 \\ 0 & -1 \end{pmatrix}$$

5. $$\begin{pmatrix} 1 & 8 \\ 5 & 2 \end{pmatrix} \times \begin{pmatrix} 3 & 4 \\ 10 & 0 \end{pmatrix}$$

6. $$3 \begin{pmatrix} -6 & 0 \\ 5 & 1 \end{pmatrix} + 2 \begin{pmatrix} -4 & 1 \\ -8 & 0 \end{pmatrix}$$

7. $$\begin{pmatrix} 6 & 5 & 2 \end{pmatrix} \times \begin{pmatrix} -4 & 0 & 5 \\ 3 & 2 & 1 \end{pmatrix}$$

8. $$\begin{pmatrix} -5 \\ 2 \\ 1 \end{pmatrix} \times \begin{pmatrix} 1 & 6 & -8 \end{pmatrix}$$

9. $$\begin{pmatrix} 5 & 11 \\ 12 & 8 \end{pmatrix} \times \begin{pmatrix} 1 & 0 \\ 0 & 1 \end{pmatrix}$$

10. If these two matrices are multiplied, what will be the number at the intersection of the second row and third column of the answer?

$$\begin{pmatrix} 3 & 6 & 0 \\ -1 & 5 & 8 \\ -7 & 0 & 2 \end{pmatrix} \times \begin{pmatrix} 1 & 7 & 4 \\ -2 & 3 & 1 \\ 5 & 4 & 6 \end{pmatrix}$$

Solutions to Problems

Chapter 1 SETS — THE ROOT OF IT ALL

Set Membership

1. $\{1,3,5,7,9\}$
2. {all the days of the week} or $\{x \mid x \text{ is a day of the week}\}$
3. ϕ
4. circle

Subsets

1. 32
2. 12
3. $\{x,y,z\}$, $\{x\}$, $\{y\}$, $\{z\}$, $\{x,y\}$, $\{x,z\}$, $\{y,z\}$, ϕ
4. True
5. False
6. True

Set Operations

1. $\{4,6\}$
2. $\{3,4,5,6,7,9,10\}$
3. $\{1,2,3,8,9,10\}$
4. $\{3,4,6,9,10\}$
5. $\{1,3,8,9,10\}$

6. $\{2\}$
7. ϕ
8. 1 if $A \neq B$
9. 0
10. ϕ
11. True
12. True

Chapter 2 RELATIONS AND FUNCTIONS—TWO SETS GET TOGETHER

Relations

1. Domain set is: $\{1,2,3,4,5\}$
   Range set is: $\{2,4,6,8,10\}$
   The second member of each pair is twice the first member.
   or The first member of each pair is one-half the second member.
   $y = 2x$

2. The second member of each pair is 1 more than twice the first member.
   $y = 2x + 1$

3.

x	y
1	0
2	0
2	1
3	0
3	1

or

x	1	2	2	3	3
y	0	0	1	0	1

Functions

1. a. 4.
   b. 5.
   c. 3.
   d. 7.
2. a. Yes, because none of these pairs has the same first member.
   b. No, because 1 appears as the first member of two different pairs. So does 5.
   c. Yes, because none of these pairs has the same first member.

Inverse Relations

1. {(4,1), (6,3), (8,5), (10,7)}.
2. a. Add 3 to the first member to obtain the second member.
   b. Subtract 3 from the first member to obtain the second member.
3. a.

Chapter 3 LOGIC—HOW TO REASON IN SYMBOLS

Conjunction

1. Jack is 42 years old and Mary is 39.
2. $p \wedge q$
3. False

Disjunction

1. Jack is 42 years old or Mary is 39.
2. $p \vee q$
3. True

Negation

1. Candy is not fattening.
   Another possible answer is: It is not true that candy is fattening.

2. I own a horse.
3. a. q'. Another possible answer is $\sim q$.
   b. $p \vee q$
   c. $p \wedge q$
   d. $p \wedge q'$
4. a. Negation
   b. Disjunction
   c. Conjunction
   d. Disjunction
   e. Negation
   f. Conjunction

The Conditional

1. You stick with me, baby.
2. You'll wear mink.
3. $p \rightarrow q$
4. False
5. True

The Biconditional

1. $p \rightarrow q$
2. If this is Christmas, then it's December 25.
3. $q \rightarrow p$
4. Yes
5. This is December 25 if and only if it's Christmas.
6. $p \longleftrightarrow q$

Chapter 4 OUR NUMBER SYSTEM—REAL AND/OR IMAGINARY

Natural Numbers

1. Googol
2. Archimedes' number
3. Googolplex
4. 13th order

Rational Numbers

1. $\frac{1}{3} + \frac{1}{2}$; $\frac{1}{4} + \frac{1}{2}$; $\frac{1}{2}$; $\frac{1}{3}$; $\frac{1}{3} + \frac{1}{3}$
2. 24
3. $\frac{5}{8}$; $\frac{7}{16}$

Irrational Numbers

1. 70 99
169 239
408 577
2. $\frac{70}{99} = .7070707\ldots$
$\frac{169}{239} = .7071129707\ldots$
$\frac{408}{577} = 707105719\ldots$
$1/\sqrt{2} = .7071068\ldots$
3. $1.414^2 = 1.999396$ $\quad 1.415^2 = 2.002225$
$1.4142^2 = 1.99996$ $\quad 1.4143^2 = 2.00024$
$1.41421^2 = 1.999989$ $\quad 1.41422^2 = 2.000018$

Negative Numbers

1. $6, \sqrt{16}$
2. $\frac{3}{4}, 0, -12, 6\frac{1}{4}, \sqrt{\frac{1}{4}}, -5\frac{1}{2}, (\frac{1}{2} + \frac{1}{4}), (\frac{1}{4} - \frac{1}{2}), 1.321\overline{56}$
3. $6, \sqrt{16}$
4. $\sqrt{5}, -\sqrt{10}, 5 - \sqrt{3}$
5. Same as problem 2

Complex Numbers

1. $i^2, i^6, -i^4, 2i^8$
2. 13; real

Chapter 5 OTHER NUMBER SYSTEMS—TWO-FINGERED MACHINES AND SIXTEEN-FINGERED MARTIANS

Binary Arithmetic

1. 12
2. 10

3. 7
4. 51
5. 124
6. 1100
7. 11100
8. 10110
9. 110001111
10. 11100100

Other Bases

1. 85
2. 41
3. 82
4. 1308
5. 333_{five}
6. 101101_{two}
7. 125_{twelve}
8. 1101001_{two}
9. 625_{eight}
10. 111010_{two}

Modular Arithmetic

1. 1
2. 4
3. 1
4. 1
5. $x = 1$
6. $x = 4$
7. $x = 1$
8. 9, 14, 19, and others
9. 11, 36, 81, and others
10. 4, and others

Modulo Ten System

1. 8
2. 1
3. 2

4.

+	0	1	2	3	4	5	6
0	0	1	2	3	4	5	6
1	1	2	3	4	5	6	0
2	2	3	4	5	6	0	1
3	3	4	5	6	0	1	2
4	4	5	6	0	1	2	3
5	5	6	0	1	2	3	4
6	6	0	1	2	3	4	5

5.

×	0	1	2
0	0	0	0
1	0	1	2
2	0	2	1

6. 12, 33, 61, and others
7. $x = 2$
8. $x = 2$

Modulo Six System

1. $x = 1, 4$
2. $x = 5, 2$
3. $x = 2$
4. 0
5. 5
6. 8, 38, 62, and others

Chapter 6 PROPERTIES OF NUMBER SYSTEMS— THE BONES OF MATHEMATICS

The ACD Laws and Arithmetic

1. True. Commutative laws for addition
2. False
3. True. Associative law for addition
4. True. Commutative law for multiplication
5. False

6. False
7. True. Associative law for multiplication
8. True. Distributive law
9. False
10. True. Distributive law

Other Number Properties

1. $-3, -\frac{1}{2}, -1, 2, \frac{4}{3}$
2. $\frac{1}{3}, 2, 1, -\frac{1}{2}, -\frac{3}{4}$
3. Inverse law for multiplication
4. Identity law for addition
5. Inverse law for addition
6. Identity law for multiplication

The ACD and Other Laws in Algebra

1. $(2a + 3b) + (5a + 7b) = (3b + 2a) + (5a + 7b)$ Commutative law
$= 3b + [2a + (5a + 7b)]$ Associative law
$= 3b + [(2a + 5a) + 7b]$ Associative law
$= 3b + [7a + 7b]$ Distributive law
$= 3b + (7b + 7a)$ Commutative law
$= (3b + 7b) + 7a$ Associative law
$= 10b + 7a$ Distributive law
$= 7a + 10b$ Commutative law

2. $ab + ac + ad = (ab + ac) + ad$
$= a(b + c) + ad$ Distributive law
$= a[(b + c) + d]$ Distributive law
$= a[b + c + d]$ Definition: $(b + c + d) = b + c + d$

3. $(a + 2b)\ (2a + b) = [(a + 2b)2a] + [(a + 2b)b]$ Distributive law
$= [2a(a + 2b)] + [b(a + 2b)]$ Commutative law
$= [2a^2 + (2a)\ (2b)] + [ba + b(2b)]$ Distributive law
$= [2a^2 + 4ab] + [ab + 2b^2]$ Commutative and Associative laws for multiplication
$= 2a^2 + 5ab + 2b^2$ Associative law for addition and definition

Mathematical Systems

1. Yes, for all
2. A. Yes B. No C. No D. Yes
3. A. Yes, 0 B. No C. Yes, 1 D. Yes, e
4. A. Yes; the inverse of 2 is 1, the inverse of 0 is 0, the inverse of 1 is 2.
   B. No element has an inverse.
   C. The inverse of 1 is 1. No other element has an inverse.
   D. The inverse of a is a, the inverse of e is e, the inverse of b is b, the inverse of c is c.

Chapter 7 SOME NUMBER THEORY—ANCIENT SUPERSTITIONS AND UNSOLVED PROBLEMS

Figurate Numbers

1. a. 7 is the gnomon

```
. . . .
------+
. . . | .
. . . | .
. . . | .
```

b. 9 is the gnomon

```
. . . . .
--------+
. . . . | .
. . . . | .
. . . . | .
. . . . | .
```

2. a. Triangular
   b. Square
   c. Triangular
   d. Square
   e. Square
   f. Triangular
   g. Square
3. 2, 5, 7, 8

Prime Numbers

1. (See Sieve of Eratosthenes)
   a. Prime
   b. Composite
   c. Prime
   d. Prime
   e. Composite
2. 53, 59, 61, 67, 71, 73, 79, 83, 89, 97

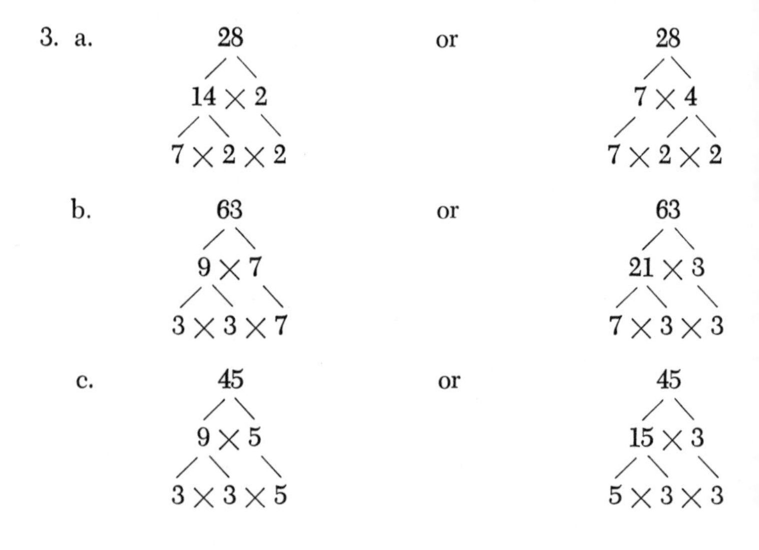

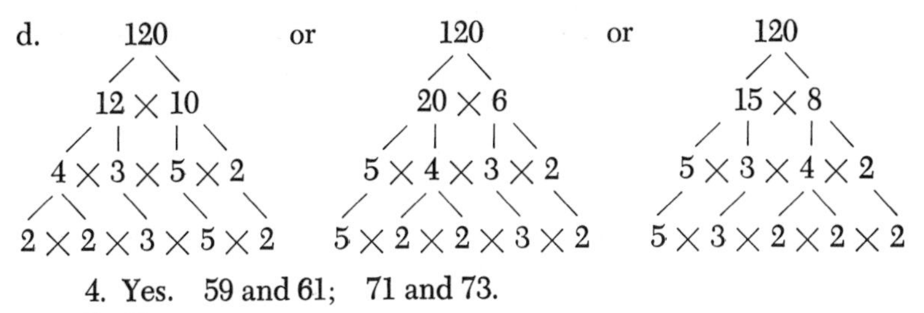

4. Yes. 59 and 61; 71 and 73.
5. 60.

Perfect Numbers and Amicable Numbers

1. a. Divisors of 46 are 1, 2, and 23. $1 + 2 + 23 = 26$.
   46 is not a perfect number.

   b. Divisors of 128 are 1, 2, 4, 8, 16, 32, 64.
   $1 + 2 + 4 + 8 + 16 + 32 + 64 = 127$.
   128 is not a perfect number.

   c. Divisors of 496 are 1, 2, 4, 8, 16, 31, 62, 124, 248.
   $1 + 2 + 4 + 8 + 16 + 31 + 62 + 124 + 248 = 496$.
   Therefore 496 is a perfect number.

2.

Divisors of 24	Divisors of 36
1	1
2	2
3	3
4	4
6	6
8	9
12	12
36	18
	55

Therefore 24 and 36 are not amicable numbers.

Fibonacci Sequence

1. 55, 89, 144, 233
2. a. .618
   b. .618
   c. .618

Chapter 8 PROBABILITY—THE SCIENCE OF LEAPING IN THE DARK

Simple Probability

1. $1/7$
2. $6/11$
3. $2/7$
4. $1/2$
5. 7 to 5; $7/12$

Compound Probability

1. $6/10$
2. $16/100$
3. $1/4 + 1/4 - 1/16 = 7/16$
4. $1/36$
5. $5/36$

Binomial Experiments

1. $3(1/2)^2(1/2) = 3/8$
2. $6(1/2)^2(1/2)^2 = 6/16$ or $3/8$
3. $1 - (5/8)^3 = 1 - 125/512 = 387/512$
4. $1 - (3/8)^3 = 1 - 27/512 = 485/512$

Chapter 9 STATISTICS—MEET MR. AVERAGE

Averages

1. 6
2. 5
3. 3

The Scatter

1. 38
2. 3
3. 4

Pictures of Data

1. a. 5
   b. 17
   c. You can't tell. The histogram shows only that there were 3 scores in the top group. It does not show precisely what these scores were.
   d. No.
2.

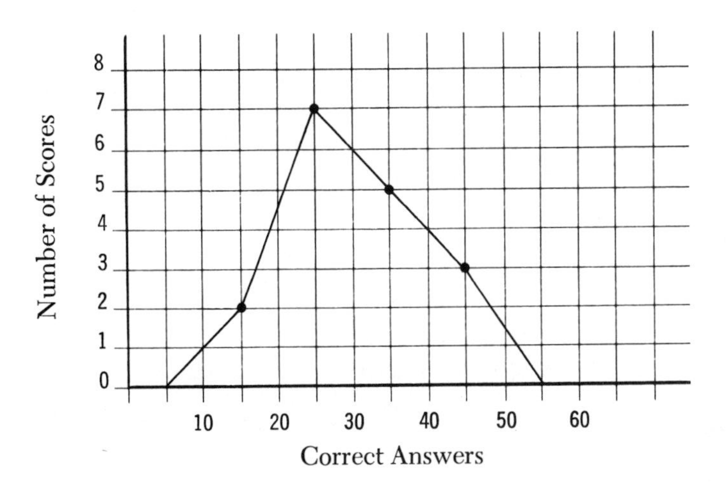

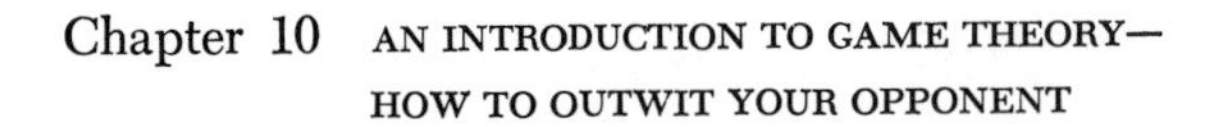

Chapter 10 AN INTRODUCTION TO GAME THEORY—HOW TO OUTWIT YOUR OPPONENT

Strategies

1.

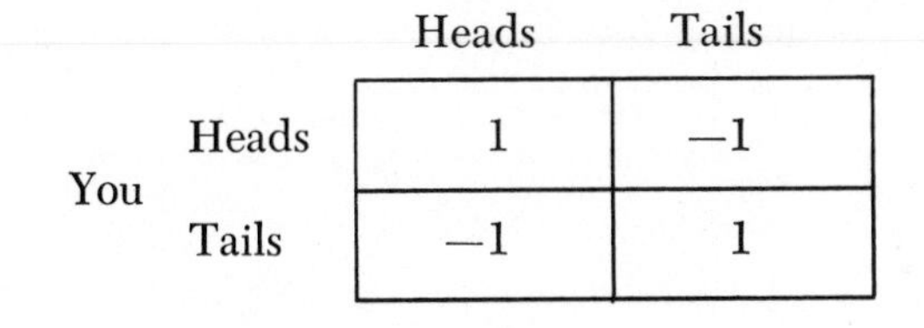

		Opponent	
		Heads	Tails
You	Heads	1	—1
	Tails	—1	1

2.

		Opponent		
		Stone	Scissors	Paper
	Stone	0	5	−1
You	Scissors	−5	0	3
	Paper	1	−3	0

Saddle Points

1. This is strictly determined, because it has a saddle point, 5.
2. Not strictly determined.
3. Strictly determined. Saddle point, 1.
4. Not strictly determined.

Chapter 11 NON-METRIC GEOMETRY—SO YOU THINK A CIRCLE HAS TO BE ROUND?

Topology

1. *b*
2. *a*
3. 20

Other Non-Metric Geometry

1. 3, non-metric
2. 4, non-metric
3. 50, metric
4. a. real b. real c. ideal; non-metric
5. $\frac{9\sqrt{3}}{4}$, metric

Chapter 12 COORDINATE GEOMETRY—THE HYBRID SUBJECT

Cartesian Coordinates

1.

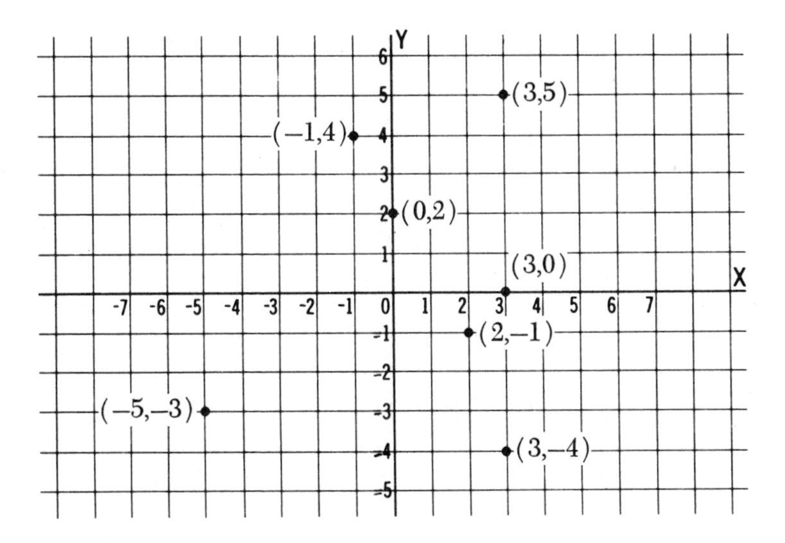

2. a. (3,4)
   b. (2,0)
   c. (4,−2)
   d. (−2,2)
   e. (−3,−4)
   f. (0,−3)
3. First; Third

Graphs of Discrete and Continuous Cases

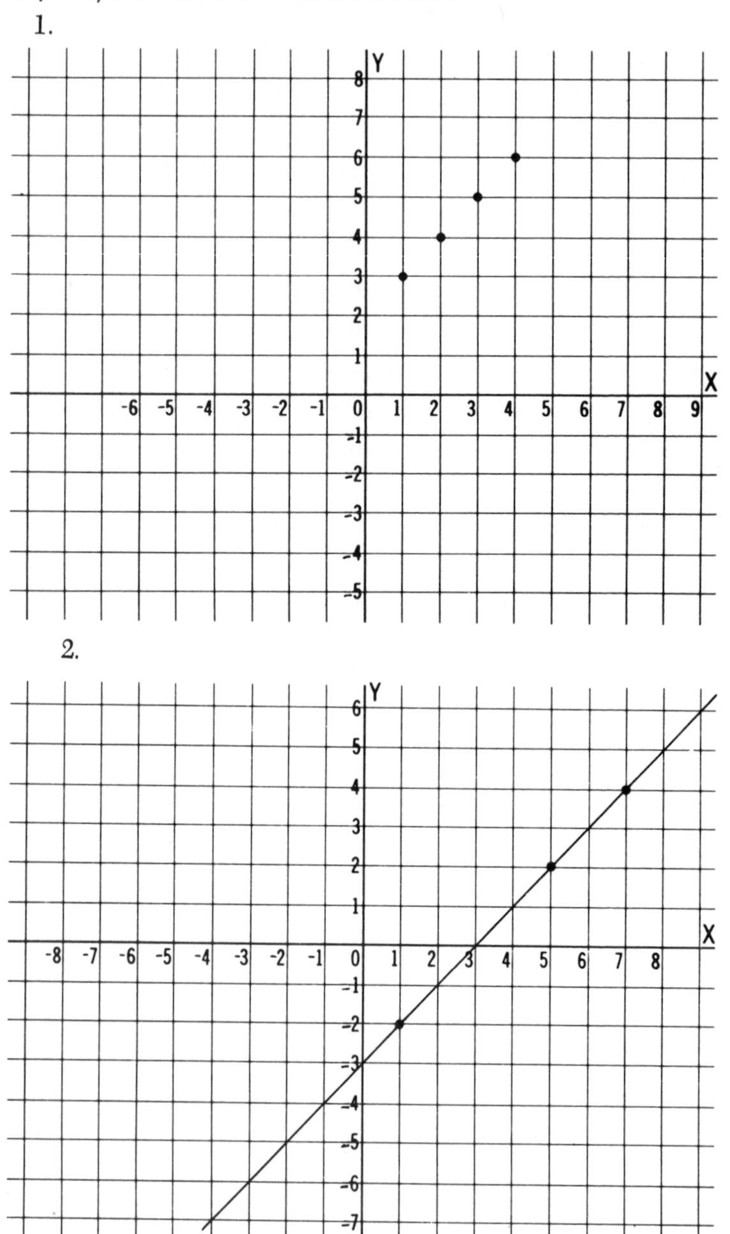

Slope

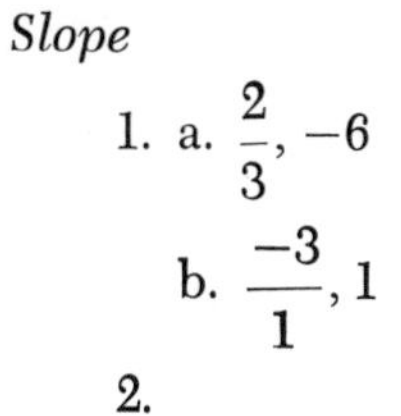

1. a. $\frac{2}{3}, -6$

   b. $\frac{-3}{1}, 1$

2.

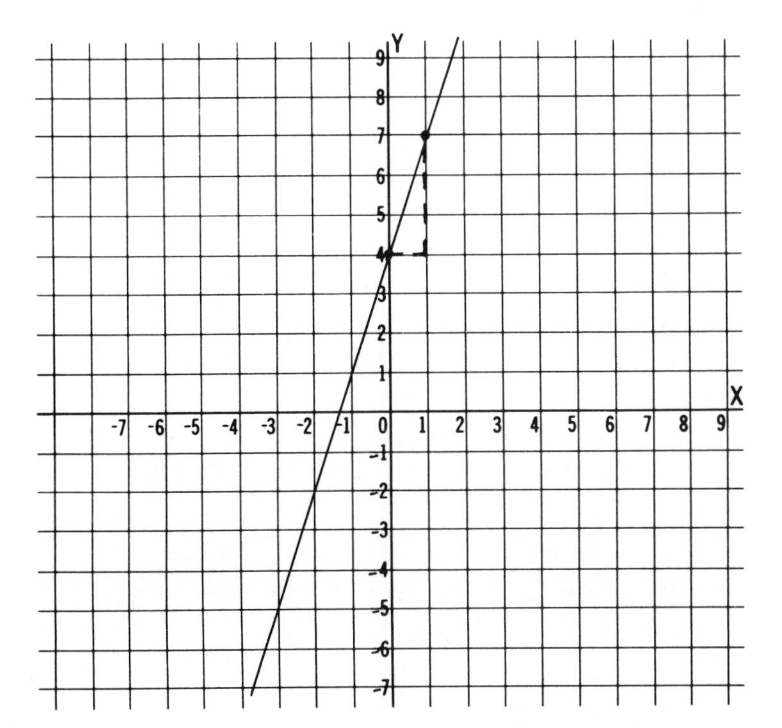

Chapter 13 INEQUALITIES AND THEIR GRAPHS—LOPSIDED SCALES

Graphing the Solution Set on a Number Line

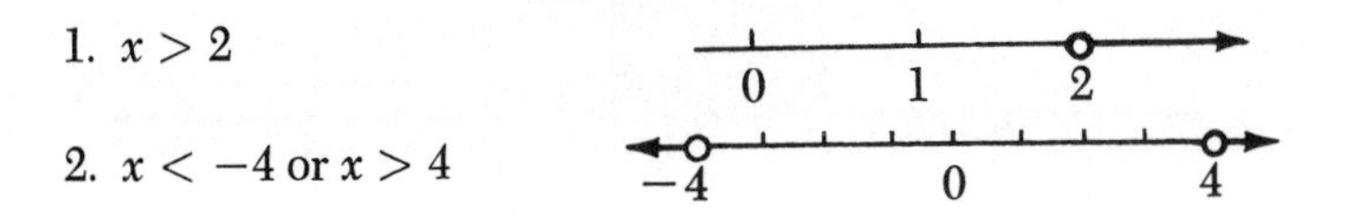

1. $x > 2$
2. $x < -4$ or $x > 4$

3. $x < -2$

4. $x \geqq -1$

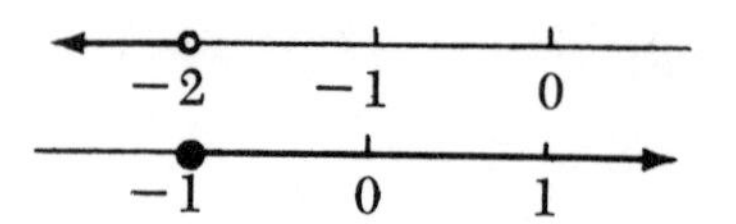

5. $x < -7$
6. No solution
7. $x \neq 7$
8. $x > 4$
9. No solution
10. Any number between 0 and 5, inclusive

Axioms of Inequalities

1. $x < 3$
2. $x > 2$
3. $x \leqq -1$
4. $x > -3$
5. $x < 1$
6. $x \leqq 5$

Graphing in a Plane

1. $x = 11$ (Number of hours for Esperanto)
   $y = 6$ (Number of hours for Early Egyp. Plumb.)

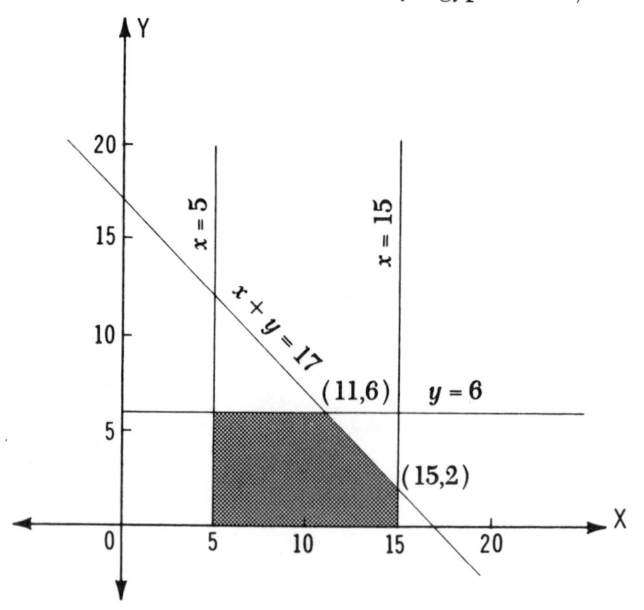

Chapter 14 VECTORS—THEY WENT THATAWAY

Scalars and Vectors

1. a. Scalar
   b. Vector
   c. Scalar
   d. Scalar
   e. Vector
2. a. West
   b. South
   c. Southwest
   d. Southeast

Vector Addition

1. 13 miles
2. 10 miles per hour
3. The magnitude of the resultant is 5 pounds. The direction of the resultant can be described by saying that it makes a 37° angle with the 4-pound force.

Vectors as Ordered Pairs

1. (3,7)
2. (2,6)
3. (6,12)
4. (5,11)

Chapter 15 MATRICES—ROWS AND COLUMNS

Operations with Matrices

1. $x = 2, y = 9$
2. $\begin{pmatrix} 4 & 13 \\ 6 & 6 \end{pmatrix}$
3. $\begin{pmatrix} 12 & 6 \\ 10 & 8 \end{pmatrix}$

4. Not possible

5. $\begin{pmatrix} 83 & 4 \\ 35 & 20 \end{pmatrix}$

6. $\begin{pmatrix} -26 & 2 \\ -1 & 3 \end{pmatrix}$

7. Not possible

8. $\begin{pmatrix} -5 & -30 & 40 \\ 2 & 12 & -16 \\ 1 & 6 & -8 \end{pmatrix}$

9. $\begin{pmatrix} 5 & 11 \\ 12 & 8 \end{pmatrix}$

10. 49

Index